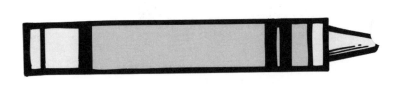

COLORFUL COUNSELING!

LIFE LESSONS LEARNED THROUGH DRAWING

Ten Reproducible Personal Booklets
For Students In Grades K-5

by
Rosanne Sheritz Sartori
&
 Rachel Hood Herrman

COUNSELORS' PAGES

10-DIGIT ISBN: 1-57543-140-8   13-DIGIT ISBN: 978-1-57543-140-6

GRAPHIC DESIGN: Cameon Funk

REPRINTED 2007
COPYRIGHT © 2006 MAR∗CO PRODUCTS, INC.
      Published by mar∗co products, inc.
      1443 Old York Road
      Warminster, PA 18974
      1-800-448-2197
      www.marcoproducts.com

PRINTED IN THE U.S.A.

Rosanne's Dedication

This book is dedicated to my sister, Chris, who I have always considered to be my "artistic sister," to the memory of my creative father; and as always— my love and thanks to my husband, Glenn, for being forever patient and kind.

Rachel's Dedication

I want to dedicate this book to the students at Coverdell Elementary in St. Charles, Missouri. I wish I had this book when I worked with you.

I also want to thank my wonderful husband, Kyle, who always supports and encourages me.

Section 1 – Self
Life Lesson Learned: I Am Special

Section 2 - Family
Life Lesson Learned: I Am A Member Of A Family

Section 3 - Friendship
Life Lesson Learned: I Can Make And Be A Friend

Section 4 - Emotional Awareness
Life Lesson Learned: I Have Feelings That I Can Share

Section 5 – Loss
Life Lesson Learned: I Can Feel Better If I Express My Feelings

Section 6 – Anger
Life Lesson Learned: I Can Calm Down When I Am Angry!

Section 7 – Fears And Worries
Life Lesson Learned: I Can Get Help When I Am Scared Or Worried

Section 8 – Behavior
Life Lesson Learned: I Am In Control Of My Own Behavior

Section 9 – School
Life Lesson Learned: I Can Be A Good Student

Section 10 - Safety First
Life Lesson Learned: I Know How To Stay Safe

COLORFUL COUNSELING!

LIFE LESSONS LEARNED THROUGH DRAWING

Introduction

An adult watching a group of children on the school playground may think that all the youngsters seem spirited, carefree, and completely happy. However the observer who got to know any one of those children might find that behind the playful facade, the child is dealing with problems and pressure and experiencing quite a bit of stress. The child's thoughts might run along these lines:

> "I am afraid to walk to school because someone might kidnap me. My mom and dad are fighting and might get a divorce. My brothers and sisters are hard to get along with, and my family is having financial difficulty. My parents and teachers are pressuring me to do better in school, and tests make me nervous. I have a very hectic schedule. Bullies are picking on me and I feel like I don't have any friends. There are terrorists in the world who want to hurt other people, and I don't feel safe."

This list might be just a *part* of what worries that particular child.

Some children seem adept at managing their own emotions and problems even at an early age. Some children are good at merely *hiding* their stress and tension, and some children act out in ways that clearly show they need adult intervention to help resolve issues that are disturbing them.

School Counseling Programs

Unlike the casual observer from the example above, counselors are aware that children of all ages have worries, problems, and stressors in their lives. Helping children learn to handle these types of issues is one of the goals of an elementary counseling program.

While counselors can't shelter or rescue children from their problems and pressures, they can help stressed children by giving them the tools they need to feel they have more power over their own lives. Counselors can teach children to become aware of their emotions, express their feelings, and solve some problems by encouraging children to get help when they need it. Adults can help children learn that they have choices over their thoughts, which can trigger the uncomfortable feelings they may be having.

Children often have difficulty using language to express their thoughts and feelings. School counselors, who have limited time with students, want to achieve productive results in a short time. Therefore, one method used by many counselors is to have children express themselves by drawing pictures.

Drawing is a familiar and comfortable means of communication for children, so it can help a child begin to express what is going on inside his/her head. A child who has learned to communicate feelings through art can later be taught to relate words to the pictures he/she has drawn. As the child matures, the pictures can eventually be eliminated. The child will then be able to use words to work through important issues and problems.

Children who begin learning these important communication skills at an early age will feel resilient, powerful, and emotionally healthy when faced with the problems and pressures of normal growth and development.

How To Use
COLORFUL COUNSELING!

Colorful Counseling! is a valuable resource for counselors. It provides an activity children enjoy and will, at the same time, teach them important life lessons. Pictures children draw to communicate their thoughts can later be used as springboards for discussion. This allows children to practice two different forms of communication.

Topics of this book's worksheets range from *self* to *school* and can be used to help children express their emotions. The worksheets may be used with individual students, small groups, and even classroom-sized groups as a means to get children thinking and talking.

The worksheets are grouped into sections suitable for every phase of an elementary counseling program. Age level, topic of discussion, and application are left to the discretion of the counselor who can use the worksheets independently, combine them for different topics of discussion, or use them to make booklets about different subject areas.

If the counselor chooses to have the student make a booklet about a particular topic, an optional cover sheet and summary worksheet have been included for each section. If the counselor is randomly using worksheets throughout the book, the section covers and summary sheets may not be needed.

The *Colorful Counseling!* reproducible worksheets are provided in two formats—black and white pages or color PDF files (found on the included CD, back inside cover). When using the program with an entire classroom, it may be more cost effective to make copies of the pages found in the book. With individuals or small groups, you may choose to print color worksheets from the PDF files.

System requirements for color worksheets: Adobe® Reader® 5.0 or newer (free download available from http://www.adobe.com). Windows 2000® or newer, Mac OS 9.0® or newer.

SECTION I – SELF
Life Lesson Learned: I Am Special

Children need to learn to appreciate their own uniqueness. Becoming aware of who they are, and what their strengths, weaknesses, and abilities are is an important part of growing to be successful adults.

Good self-esteem is also important. Children need to believe they have some power over their world. Having good self-esteem does not mean that a child believes he/she is better than anyone else, but each child needs to feel that he/she is as good as everyone else!

Some children are confident and self-assured from an early age. Some need to be nurtured and encouraged. Children who are constantly comparing themselves to others can usually find someone better-looking, smarter, or more athletic. The habit of comparison can lead to feelings of worthlessness, shyness, or inferiority.

If a counselor can encourage children to appreciate their own worth while continuing to work to the best of their ability, those children will achieve more success in school as well as in life.

The pages in this section and in the following sections can be used to make small booklets or be used one at a time. The worksheets can be used with individual students, small groups, or in classroom guidance. Mix and match the sheets and sit with the children as they complete the pages. Listening to what the children say as they draw will let them know the counselor is interested in them and will help them feel special and learn important communication skills.

SELF

DIRECTIONS

SELF: PAGE 1-1
ALL ABOUT ME (Title Page)
Have the children complete this page by filling in the blanks and coloring the title words (*All About Me*). Encourage children to write their full name and, if necessary, learn to spell all parts of their name and be proud that the name was selected especially for them. Ask how the name was selected. If children do not know, encourage them to find out.

SELF: PAGE 1-2
SOMEONE SPECIAL
Have the children draw themselves and use crayons to show the color of their hair, skin, and eyes. You may want to have a mirror available for the children.

SELF: PAGE 1-3
A POSTER ALL ABOUT ME!
Children may use this page to write or draw what they would like others to know about them. Encourage children to put as many ideas as they can into this special poster.

SELF: PAGE 1-4
MY WISHES!
Tell the children to dream big for themselves! What do they wish would happen in the future? The sky is the limit when a person is making wishes! Have the children write or draw their wishes in the three clouds on the page.

SELF: PAGE 1-5
MY FAVORITE THINGS
Tell the children that everyone has likes and dislikes and you are interested in knowing about the things they like. In each section, have the children draw a small picture of something they like. Have the children share their favorites with the group. If the sheet is being used with an individual child, the adult may complete a sheet as the child is drawing, then compare the selections.

SELF: PAGE 1-6

MY STRENGTHS/MY WEAKNESSES

Tell the children that everyone has strengths—areas in which a person succeeds, and weaknesses—areas in which a person must work hard to do well. The adult should go first, completing the sheet honestly. Complete the activity by writing your weaknesses on the mountains. Write your strengths in the burst above the mountain. The adult should then share his/her sheet so the children can see that weaknesses are nothing to be embarrassed about—just a part of being human. Have the children complete the worksheet, encouraging them to realize that everyone can feel proud of his/her strengths and should not stop trying to improve on his/her weaknesses. The only failure is to stop trying!

SELF: PAGE 1-7

THIS IS THE ME I WANT TO BE!

Tell the children that they must set their standards high and strive to be the best they can be. Have the children set goals to do something they don't know how to do, then draw a picture showing that they have succeeded!

SELF: PAGE 1-8

I WANT TO RESPECT THE PERSON IN THE MIRROR

Tell the children that they will find self-respect if they know they are doing the "right thing." Have them think about a time they had a choice between doing something that would affect others positively or doing something that would have hurt another person. Then have the children draw in the mirror a picture of themselves proudly making the better choice.

SELF: PAGE 1-9

TIME CAPSULE

Have the children draw themselves in the future. What will their careers be? Tell them to draw a picture of themselves as adults, doing the jobs they think they would enjoy.

SELF: PAGE 1-10

LIFE LESSON LEARNED – I AM SPECIAL

As the children color the words *I Am Special*, reinforce the ideas covered in this section. Everyone is special and unique, has strengths and weaknesses, can feel proud when making good choices, and can dream about the future!

ALL ABOUT ME

There is only one person who is just like me,
And I am very special, as I'm sure you can see.
I have a lot of strengths and some true ability,
That will be enough to take me where I always want to be.
Good attitude with effort is a big important key,
And I will find success ... that I guarantee.

MY FULL NAME IS

_____

MY BIRTHDAY IS

_____

SELF 1-1

Someone Special

A Poster All About ME!

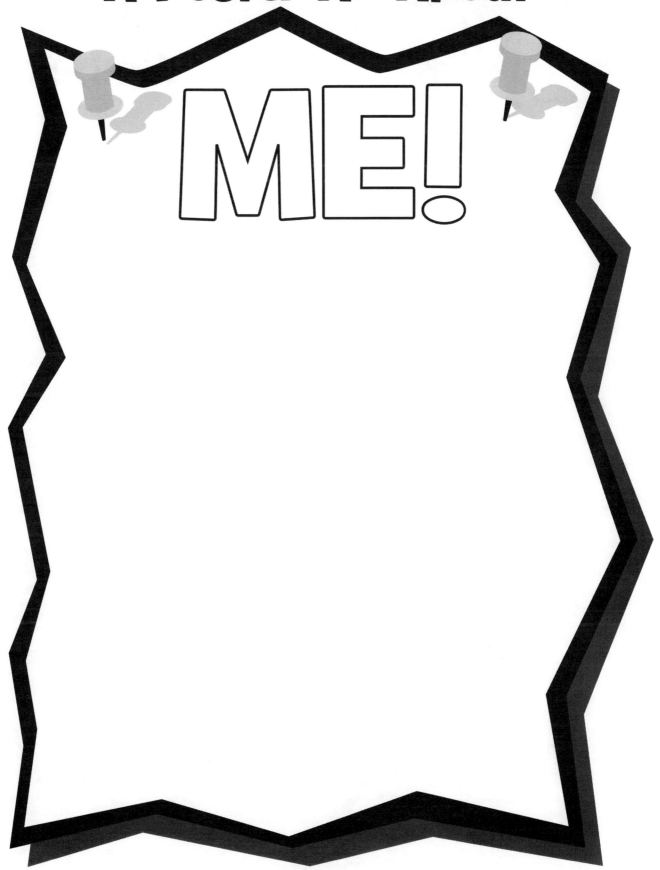

THE SKY'S THE LIMIT!

MY
Wishes!

My Favorite Things

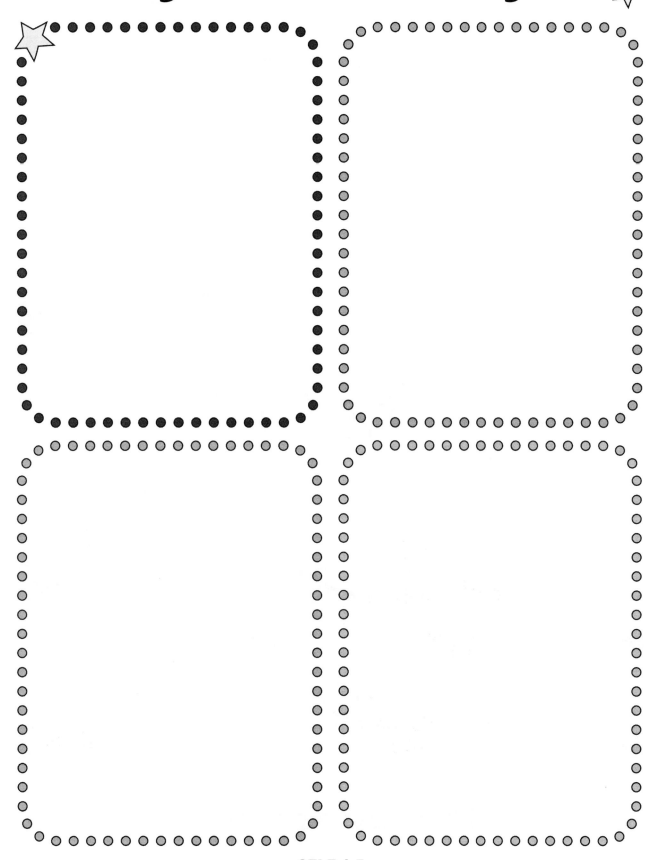

My Strengths

My Weaknesses

This Is The Me I Want To Be!

I Want To Respect The Person In The Mirror

Time Capsule

LIFE LESSON LEARNED

I AM SPECIAL

SECTION 2 - FAMILY
Life Lesson Learned: I Am A Member Of A Family

Every family is unique. Children are often embarrassed or ashamed if their families seem to differ from the norm. When helping children cope with their family situations, it can be helpful to emphasize that every family is one of a kind.

Encourage the students to draw special aspects of their families and homes. The drawings will provide the counselor with factual information about the student's family and will serve as a springboard for discussion about feelings surrounding each family situation and coping mechanisms already in place.

As with all sections, these pages may be used independently or put into a booklet for the child.

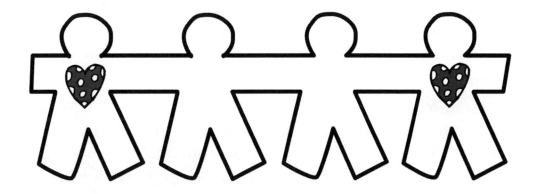

DIRECTIONS

FAMILY: PAGE 2-1
MY FAMILY IS UNIQUE (Title Page)

Discuss the definition of *unique* with the children. Help them understand that every family is unique, just as each child is unique. Listen to what the children say as they color in the letters on this title sheet. The children may give insight to family situations or problems.

FAMILY: PAGE 2-2
THIS IS MY FAMILY

Have the children draw pictures of their family members. Encourage the children to draw the people regarded as family, even if they don't live in the same house.

FAMILY: PAGE 2-3
THIS IS WHERE WE LIVE

Have the children write their full addresses on the mailbox. If they divide time between two homes, make two copies of the page for each child and have them write both addresses and draw both residences. If appropriate, converse with the children about their feelings about where they live and about having to go back and forth between two homes.

FAMILY: PAGE 2-4
MY FAMILY HAS PROBLEMS

Because children can be dealing with a variety of issues within their families, this page includes a "catchall title." The children should draw their depictions of whatever is happening at home (e.g., parent in jail, parent addicted to drugs or alcohol, parents separated or divorced, etc.)

FAMILY: PAGE 2-5
FAMILY ARGUMENTS

Families under stress are often plagued by frequent arguments. Children may be bystanders or "flies on the wall" while these arguments occur. The children can draw the arguments and/or the reasons for the arguments, while the counselor makes the point that children are not usually responsible for arguments parents have.

FAMILY: PAGE 2-6
MY FAMILY HAS FINANCIAL PROBLEMS

Arguments over money is a major cause of divorce in the United States. If this page applies, have the children draw inside the piggy bank what their family argues about. (e.g., frivolous spending, debt, gambling, etc.)

FAMILY: PAGE 2-7
I CAN MAKE MYSELF FEEL BETTER

This page can help the counselor gauge the child's ability to cope. Prompt children to draw ways they can make themselves feel better. Explain that while children cannot change the family's situation, they can do something to improve how they are feeling. Tell the children that these coping skills can be used with any situation that causes emotional discomfort.

FAMILY: PAGE 2-8
I HAVE A NEW BROTHER/SISTER

While the arrival of a new sibling is not necessarily a family problem, this situation can disrupt a child's life in many ways. Discuss with the children the multiple changes a new sibling will bring and have them draw a few of those changes. Also encourage children to take pride in being a big brother or sister.

FAMILY: PAGE 2-9
I DO/DON'T GET ALONG WITH MY SIBLINGS BECAUSE...

Like it or not, brothers and sisters are here to stay! On this page, children may draw what they believe to be their relationship with siblings. Have the children circle whichever title word—do or don't—best describes their relationship with their siblings, then draw what comes to mind. As the children draw, encourage talk about what strains the relationship with a brother or sister and what can help it stay strong.

FAMILY: PAGE 2-10
THESE ARE THE DREAMS I HAVE FOR MY FAMILY

In each bubble, the children may draw what they would like to see happen to their family in the future. The counselor may talk with the children about family problems. Be sure to make the point that problems need not be passed down from generation to generation.

FAMILY: PAGE 2-11
THESE ARE THE THINGS MY FAMILY LIKES TO DO TOGETHER
Inside the box of popcorn, the children may draw the activities they like to do with family members. Quality family time can be spent doing anything from reading books to going to the grocery store.

FAMILY: PAGE 2-12
I LIKE BEING A MEMBER OF MY FAMILY BECAUSE...
Conclude this family booklet on a positive note. Prompt the children to draw the positive aspects about their families.

FAMILY: PAGE 2-13
LIFE LESSON LEARNED - I AM A MEMBER OF A FAMILY
As the children color the words *I Am A Member Of A Family*, reinforce the ideas covered in this section. Every person comes from a family. Help the children take pride in being a part of a unique, one-of-a-kind family.

MY FAMILY IS UNIQUE

I am a member of a family with ties that bond like glue.
I'll do my part to get along and together we'll get through!

MY NAME IS

_____

GRADE _____ DATE _____

FAMILY 2-1

This Is My Family

This Is Where We Live

My Family Has Problems

Family Arguments

No family is perfect. Here's what is going on in my family:

FAMILY 2-5

My Family Has
Financial Problems

I Can Make Myself Feel Better

**While I can't solve my family's problems,
I can help myself feel better and less stressed.**

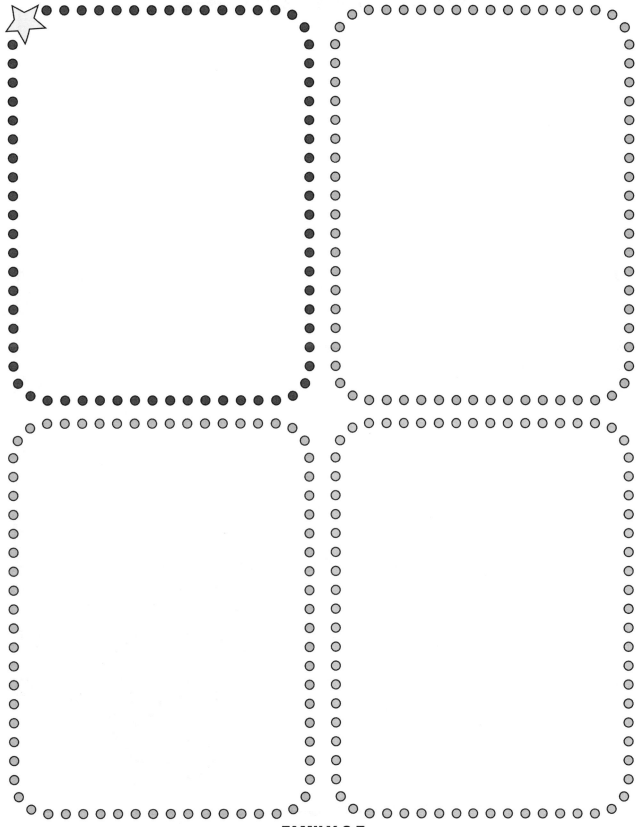

I have a new brother/sister named _____

HERE IS HOW I FEEL:

I Do/Don't Get Along With
My Siblings Because...

FAMILY 2-10
COLORFUL COUNSELING! © 2006 MAR✶CO PRODUCTS, INC. 1-800-448-2197

These Are The Things My Family Likes To Do Together

FAMILY 2-11

I Like Being A Member Of My Family Because...

LIFE LESSON LEARNED

I AM A MEMBER OF A FAMILY

SECTION 3 – FRIENDSHIP
Life Lesson Learned: I Can Make And Be A Friend

All people have a need to be connected with others and learn to form those connections in childhood. Having solid friendships can help children feel good about themselves. Children who lack quality friendships may feel alone and isolated. The following pages are based on the assumption that the child is having difficulty forming connections with other children. Use the pages to help children explore ways to make friends and maintain friendships.

As the children follow the prompts at the top of the page and draw, the counselor may identify friendship skills that they need to strengthen or develop. The drawings may also be used as an impetus for role-plays.

COLORFUL COUNSELING! © 2006 MAR∗CO PRODUCTS, INC. 1-800-448-2197

DIRECTIONS

FRIENDSHIP: PAGE 3-1
I AM A FRIEND (Title Page)
As the children color in the letters and add identifying information, the counselor should discuss how the following pages will help them learn ways to make friends and maintain friendships.

FRIENDSHIP: PAGE 3-2
THESE ARE MY FRIENDS
In the picture frames, have the children draw pictures of their friends. If children hesitate or claim they have no friends, encourage them to think of people they enjoy being around and would like to have as friends.

FRIENDSHIP: PAGE 3-3
I CAN MAKE A FRIEND
Inside the soccer ball, have the children draw ways to make a friend. (Smile, be confident and invite someone to play, introduce themselves, apologize when appropriate, let a friend go first, take turns, use appropriate eye contact, etc.)

FRIENDSHIP: PAGE 3-4
I CAN KEEP A FRIEND
In each section of the bicycle wheel, have the children draw or write a different way to keep a friend. (Say nice things, listen, give compliments, respect personal space and property, let your friend play with others, share, show interest, etc.)

FRIENDSHIP: PAGE 3-5
THERE IS A NEW STUDENT AT SCHOOL … ME!
This page is similar to page 3-3, but is for the new student. Being a new student can be a frightening experience. In this special situation, children who previously had many friends may find themselves alone. The counselor can help these children think of ways to meet new friends in the new school, then have them draw some things they can do to make new friends.

FRIENDSHIP: PAGE 3-6
THIS IS WHAT I ENJOY DOING INSIDE WITH MY FRIENDS
In the house, the children can draw indoor activities they enjoy doing with other people. Emphasize that good friends take turns doing what the other person likes to do.

FRIENDSHIP: PAGE 3-7
THIS IS WHAT I ENJOY DOING OUTSIDE WITH MY FRIENDS
The children can draw favorite outdoor activities that they enjoy doing with other people. Remind the children that good friends take turns doing what the other person likes to do.

FRIENDSHIP: PAGE 3-8
I KNOW HOW TO HANDLE GOSSIP AND RUMORS
Gossip and rumors destroy current and potential friendships. In the bubble, have the children draw ways to behave when someone comes to them with a rumor or a bit of gossip (saying "I don't like to gossip" or "I don't like to spread rumors," etc.).

FRIENDSHIP: PAGE 3-9
I KNOW HOW TO HANDLE BULLIES!
Discuss the definition of a *bully*. (Someone who misuses power to put another person down physically, emotionally, or verbally.) Ask the children to think of ways that they could stop a bully from picking on them. Have them draw their ideas in the sections on the page.

FRIENDSHIP: PAGE 3-10
I KNOW HOW TO SETTLE ARGUMENTS PEACEFULLY
No matter how great their friendship, two people will sometimes experience conflict and disagreements. While the counselor explains that friends may not always see eye to eye, the children can draw a way they know to resolve disagreements in each section of the peace sign. (Calming down, admitting when they are wrong, apologizing, compromising, taking turns with ideas, etc.)

FRIENDSHIP: PAGE 3-11
I KNOW HOW TO PLAY FAIR
Young children get into arguments over toys and games. In each section of the tic-tac-toe board, have the children draw a way to play fair or decide who should take the first turn. (Use childhood rhymes or "Rock/Scissors/Paper," vote, be generous, take turns, share, etc.)

FRIENDSHIP: PAGE 3-12
WE ARE ALIKE AND DIFFERENT
This activity is performed with a partner but can be adapted for completion by one child. Instruct the child to write his/her name on one line and the name of a friend (or desired friend) on the other line. In the part of the circles that intersect, each child should draw the similarities he/she shares with his/her friend (or desired friend). In the outer part of the circles, each child should draw differences between him/herself and his/her friend (or desired friend). (Anyone who is not sure of this information could ask the friend or just put down the facts he/she knows for sure.) Each circle should include the child's age and the friend's age, talent, family, favorite animal, sport, pets, favorite TV show, and favorite books. The counselor may take this opportunity to discuss that no two people are exactly alike and why that is a good thing. The counselor should encourage the children to celebrate their differences.

FRIENDSHIP: PAGE 3-13
LIFE LESSON LEARNED - I CAN MAKE AND BE A FRIEND
As the children color in this concluding statement, the counselor should review the character traits that make a good friend.

I AM A FRIEND

I want to have friends,
So I know what I must do …
Along with jokes and laughter,
I must be a friend who's true.

What do I have to offer
To make you a longtime friend?
Kindness, warmth, and caring,
A helping hand, which I'll extend.

MY NAME IS

_____

GRADE _____ DATE _____

FRIENDSHIP 3-1

These Are My Friends

FRIENDSHIP 3-3
COLORFUL COUNSELING! © 2006 MAR∗CO PRODUCTS, INC. 1-800-448-2197

I Can Keep A Friend

There Is A New Student At School ... ME!

Here's how I can make new friends:

 **Idea #1**

 **Idea #2**

Idea #3

This Is What I Enjoy Doing INSIDE With My Friends

This Is What I Enjoy Doing OUTSIDE With My Friends

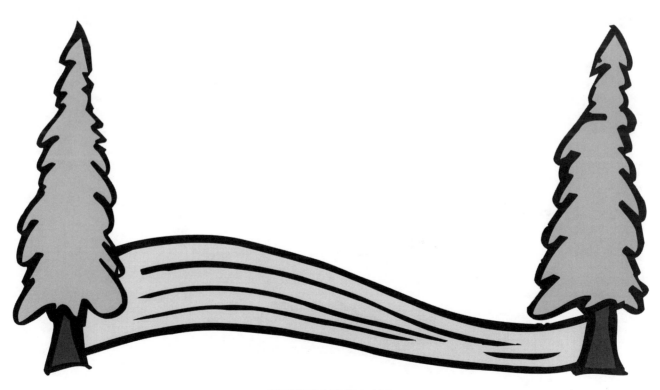

I Know How To Handle Gossip And Rumors

I Know How To Handle
BULLIES!

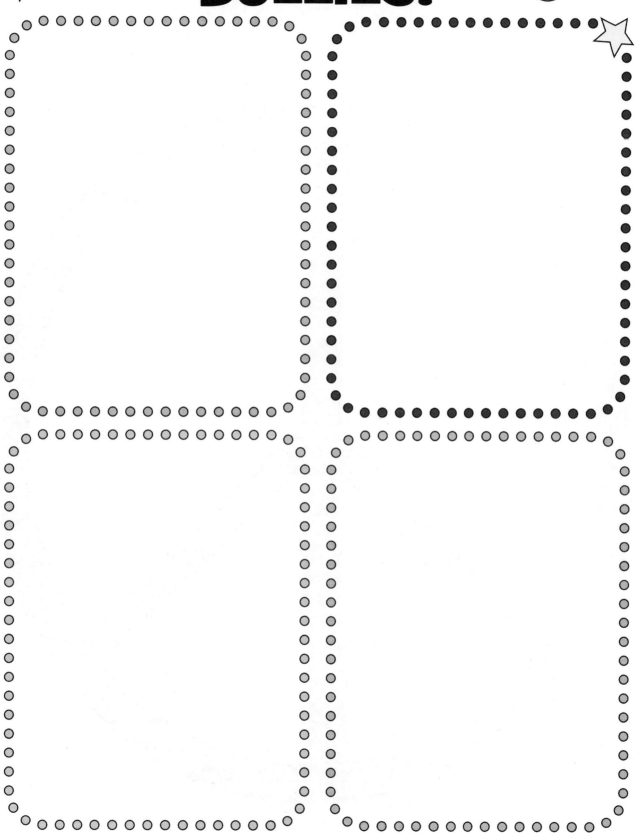

I Know How To Settle Arguments
PEACEFULLY

I Know How To Play Fair

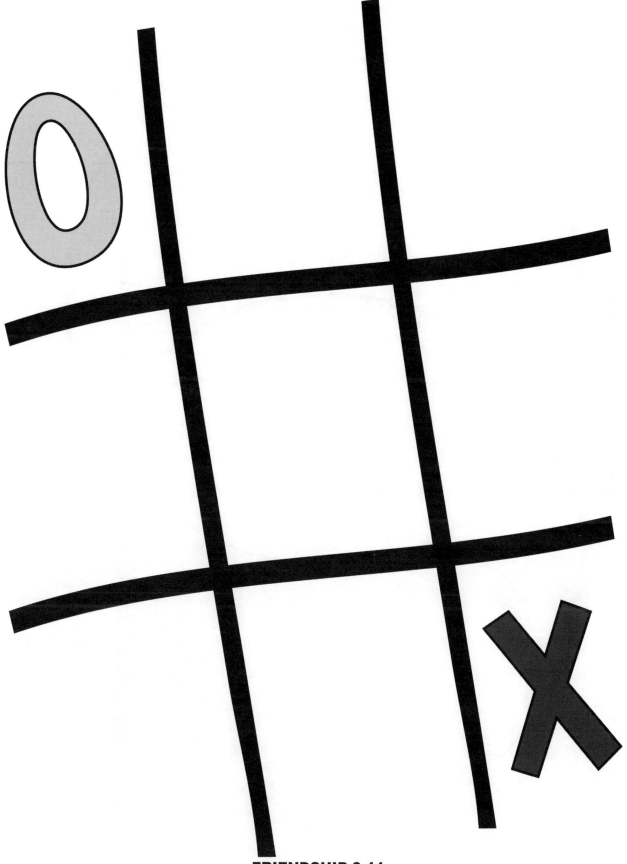

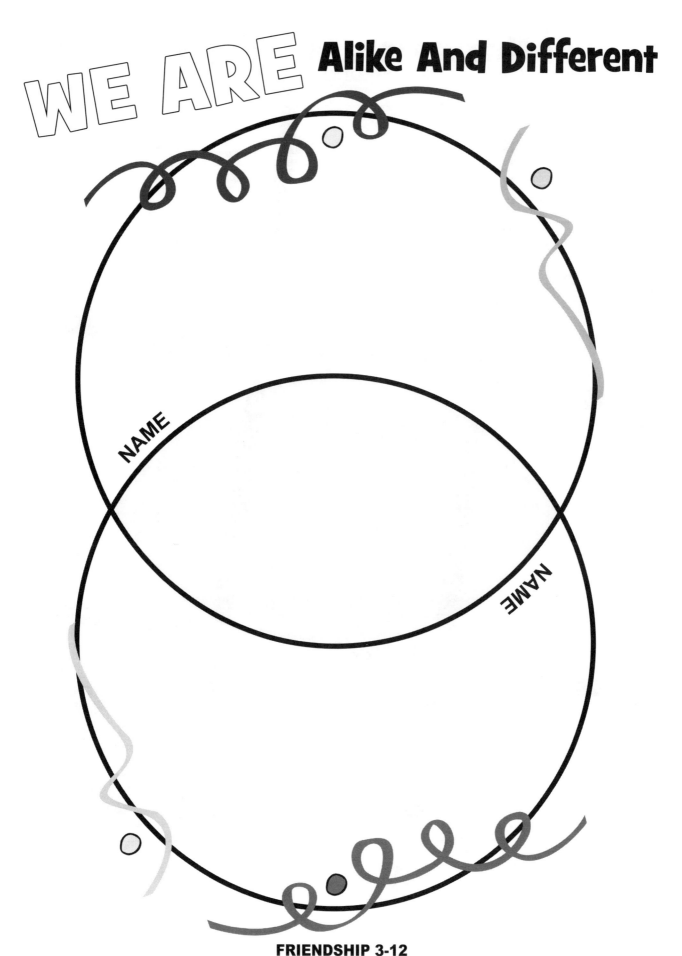

WE ARE Alike And Different

NAME

NAME

LIFE LESSON LEARNED

I CAN MAKE AND BE A FRIEND

SECTION 4 – EMOTIONAL AWARENESS
Life Lesson Learned: I Have Feelings That I Can Share

Emotional awareness is a key component of good emotional health. Children who develop a large "feelings vocabulary" and learn ways to express their emotions are less likely to become frustrated and act out in inappropriate ways. A counselor should encourage children to increase their vocabulary and go beyond *glad, mad, sad,* and *scared* to describe what they feel. Teach children that many words can express the nuances of what a person is feeling. Tell children that developing an extensive "feelings vocabulary" will help them accurately describe what is going on in their minds.

If asked where their feelings come from, children may say their feelings come from their heart. The counselor should teach children that feelings come from their brains and that their thoughts determine how they feel about a situation. Teach children that if they can alter their thoughts, their feelings can also be changed. Learning this skill can help them cope with many stresses in life.

The following pages have been designed to help children develop an extensive "feelings vocabulary," identify what they feel when events occur, and learn ways to alter how they are feeling. Because emotional awareness develops as children mature, some of the following pages have been separated for younger and older children. As in other sections, the counselor may use the pages independently or bound together as a booklet.

An extensive list of feelings words (page 4-12) included in this section may be used when children are searching for an appropriate word. Take some time to go through the list of words. Teach the children the definitions and have them practice the appropriate use of the words.

EMOTIONAL AWARENESS

DIRECTIONS

EMOTIONAL AWARENESS: PAGE 4-1
EVERYONE HAS FEELINGS (Title Page)
As the children color the title page, the counselor can teach and reinforce important emotional concepts: that everyone has *feelings*, which are also called *emotions*. The counselor should stress that feelings originate in a person's brain, though some people mistakenly think the heart has something to do with feelings. Tell the children that how they think about a situation will affect how they feel about it. Use the following examples: One child might be afraid of a thunderstorm and another might be exhilarated. What is the difference between them? (The first child is thinking, "This storm could hurt me. I saw on the news once that a whole neighborhood was destroyed by a storm." The second child could be thinking, "I am safe inside and I love to watch the lightning bolts and hear the big booms!" The different thoughts cause different feelings!)

EMOTIONAL AWARENESS: PAGE 4-2
FEELINGS ALPHABET
As the children read or color in each letter, challenge them to name a feeling that begins with that letter. If they cannot do this, use the list of feeling words on page 4-12 to identify a feeling and describe a situation that might make the children feel that way.

EMOTIONAL AWARENESS: PAGE 4-3
TODAY I FEEL ... (For Younger Children)
Review the feelings shown on the cartoon faces. Ask the children to identify events that make them feel that way and the way they are feeling today. Have them color the face with the color they think reflects that feeling. Tell them that even though there are no right or wrong answers, some people associate colors with feelings. (For example: The color red might go with anger. Blue is often used as another word for sad. Happy might be a bright color, such as yellow, etc.)

EMOTIONAL AWARENESS: PAGE 4-4
TODAY I FEEL ... (For Older Children)
Using the *Feelings Alphabet* on page 4-2 as a guide, ask the children to write or a draw in the circle a picture of how they feel. Then have them draw in the rectangle the reasons they feel as they do.

EMOTIONAL AWARENESS: PAGE 4-5
I FEEL ... WHEN ... (For Younger Children)
In each circle, have the children draw a feelings face and/or write a feelings word on the blank line. In the rectangle to the right of each circle, have the children draw a situation that makes them feel that way.

EMOTIONAL AWARENESS: PAGE 4-6
I FEEL ... WHEN ... (For Older Children)
Have the children complete the sentence fragments. At the bottom of the page, have them fill in the name of someone they can talk with about how they are feeling. Explain that sharing feelings with a trusted person can bring relief if only because those feelings are no longer secret. Sometimes the person can help with the situation that triggered the feelings.

EMOTIONAL AWARENESS: PAGE 4-7
CHANGING HOW I FEEL
This page reinforces the idea that people can change how they are feeling by changing their thoughts. Have the children think of a feeling they would like to change. The situation does not have to be from "sad to happy" but perhaps "nervous to relaxed" or "angry to calm." Tell the children to draw a "feelings face" in the circle on the left and its opposite feeling in the circle on the right. Then have them talk about when these feelings occur. Have them color the "feelings faces" with colors they think represent those feelings. Brainstorm orally with the children ways to go from the first feeling to the opposite feeling. Have the children draw the option they like best in the rectangle.

EMOTIONAL AWARENESS: PAGE 4-8
CONFLICTING FEELINGS
Sometimes people have feelings which conflict with each other. A person may feel two ways about a situation. For example, a child may be relieved that his/her parents are getting a divorce because they argued so much, but sad because he/she will no longer live with one of them. On this page, brainstorm with the children situations in which they have encountered conflicting feelings. Have them draw the feelings faces as best they can. Emphasize that conflicting feelings are normal.

EMOTIONAL AWARENESS: PAGE 4-9
FEELINGS FACES
Throughout the discussion, emphasize that everyone has feelings. While feelings originate in the brain, they are shown and experienced throughout the body. Discuss with the children that feelings often show on a person's face. Explain that it will help them get along if they can look at the faces of others and be "feelings detectives." Using facial clues to identify the feelings in other people will show that they care about others and they will have more friends. In the circles on this page, have the children draw as many feeling faces as they can. If the children can write, have them write the name of each feeling on the line below each circle. The counselor can be the model! Have fun!

EMOTIONAL AWARENESS: PAGE 4-10
MY BODY TELLS ME WHAT I'M FEELING
Sometimes feelings can be confusing. Children may not be sure what they are feeling. In this case, they might get additional clues as to what they are feeling from what is going on inside their bodies. Are their fists and teeth clenched? Then perhaps they are angry. Do their stomachs hurt? If so, perhaps they are sad or worried. Do they have "butterflies" in their stomachs? Perhaps they are nervous. Using the body outline, tell the children to write or draw symptoms they have felt in each body part and name the feelings that go with these symptoms. A child who cannot write may draw the feelings faces or symbols.

EMOTIONAL AWARENESS: PAGE 4-11
I CAN SHARE MY FEELINGS
Have the children draw people with whom they feel comfortable sharing their feelings. Emphasize the importance of doing so!

EMOTIONAL AWARENESS: PAGE 4-12
A LIST OF FEELINGS WORDS
Review meanings and use of the words on this page. Use the list as needed.

EMOTIONAL AWARENESS: PAGE 4-13
LIFE LESSON LEARNED - I HAVE FEELINGS THAT I CAN SHARE
As the children color the message, review what they have learned about feelings. All people have feelings, feelings come from the brain, a person who can change how he/she thinks can change how he/she feels about a situation, feelings are shown on the face and experienced throughout the body, and it is helpful to share feelings with people who care.

EMOTIONAL AWARENESS

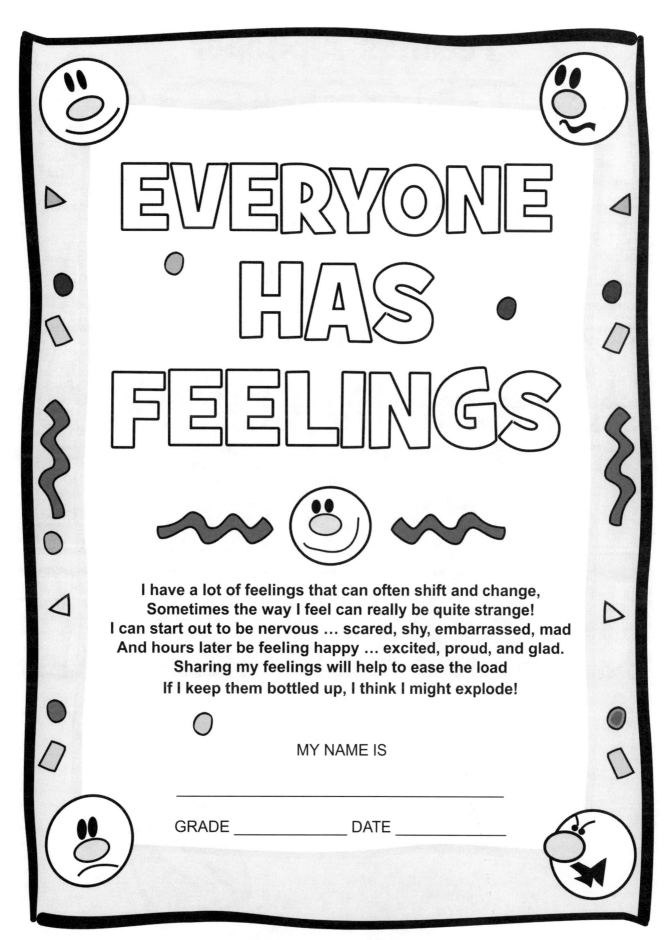

EVERYONE HAS FEELINGS

I have a lot of feelings that can often shift and change,
Sometimes the way I feel can really be quite strange!
I can start out to be nervous … scared, shy, embarrassed, mad
And hours later be feeling happy … excited, proud, and glad.
Sharing my feelings will help to ease the load
If I keep them bottled up, I think I might explode!

MY NAME IS

_____

GRADE _____ DATE _____

EMOTIONAL AWARENESS 4-1

Feelings Alphabet

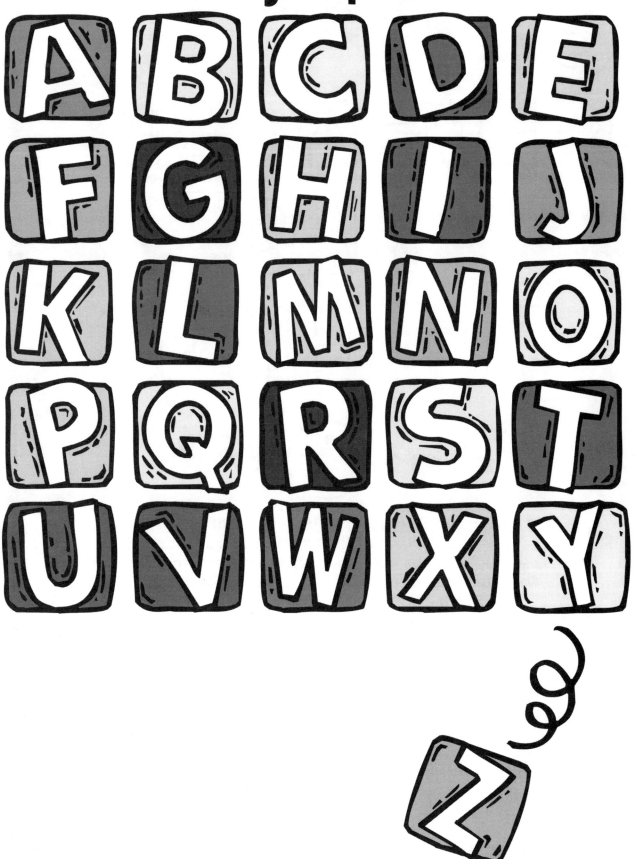

Today I Feel ...

ANGRY

SCARED

CONFUSED

HAPPY

EXCITED

SAD

SILLY

PROUD

WORRIED

EMOTIONAL AWARENESS 4-3
COLORFUL COUNSELING! © 2006 MAR*CO PRODUCTS, INC. 1-800-448-2197

Today I Feel ...

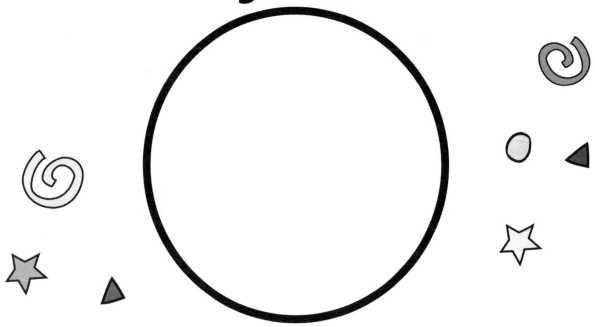

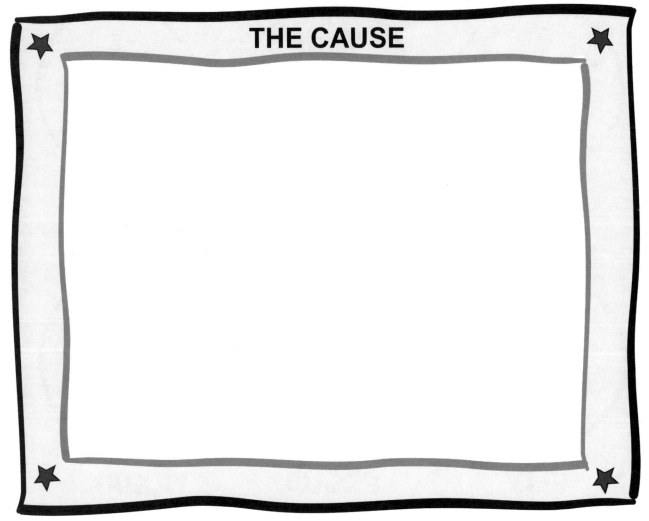

THE CAUSE

I Feel ...　　When ...

FEELINGS WORD _____

FEELINGS WORD _____

FEELINGS WORD _____

EMOTIONAL AWARENESS 4-5
COLORFUL COUNSELING! © 2006 MAR✶CO PRODUCTS, INC. 1-800-448-2197

 # I Feel ... When ...

I feel angry when _____ .

I feel sad when _____ .

I feel embarrassed when _____ .

I feel happy when _____ .

I feel proud when _____ .

I feel frustrated when _____ .

I feel afraid when _____ .

I feel excited when _____ .

My feelings get hurt when _____ .

I feel nervous when _____ .

I feel guilty when _____ .

I can talk to_____about my feelings.

EMOTIONAL AWARENESS 4-6
COLORFUL COUNSELING! © 2006 MAR∗CO PRODUCTS, INC. 1-800-448-2197

Changing How I
FEEL

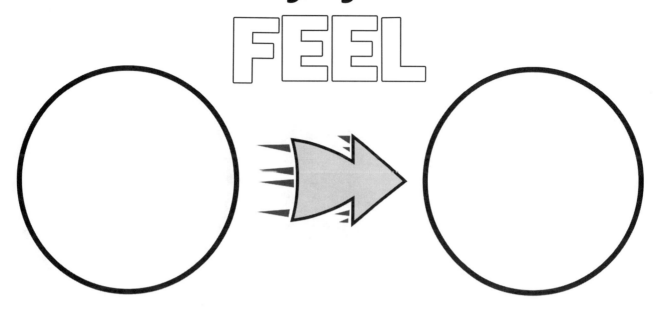

HOW COULD I CHANGE?

Conflicting Feelings

I Feel...

When _____

I Feel...

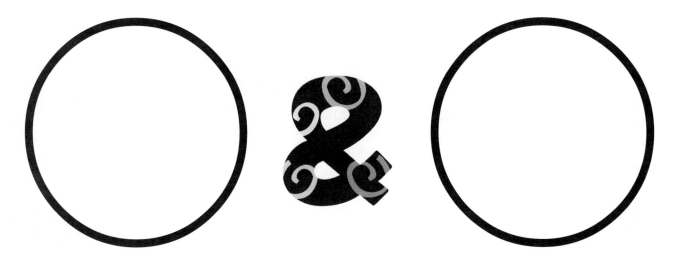

When _____

Feelings Faces

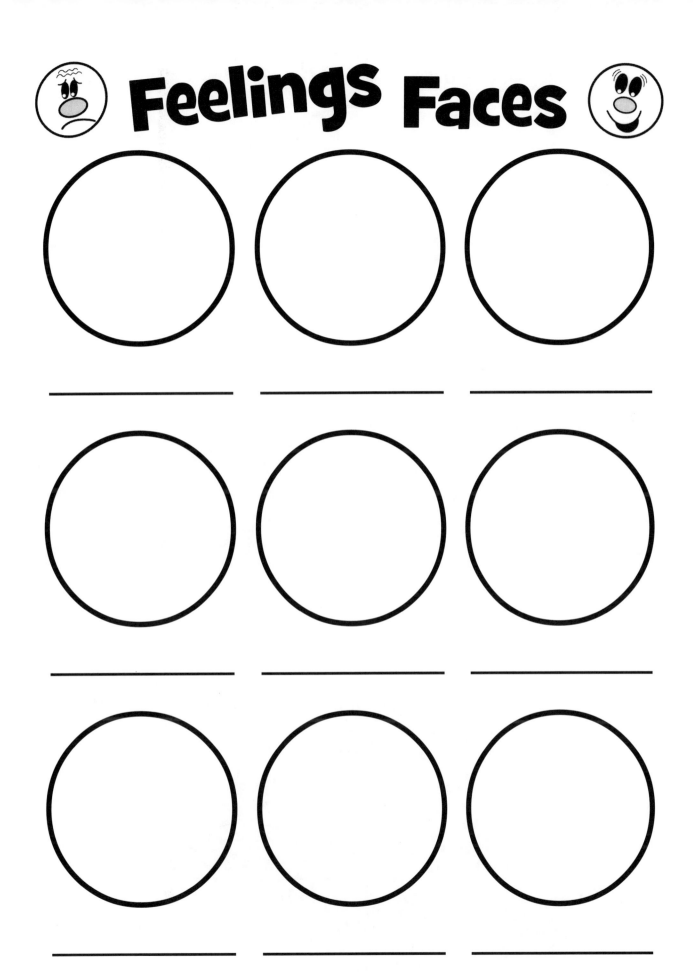

My Body Tells Me What I'm Feeling

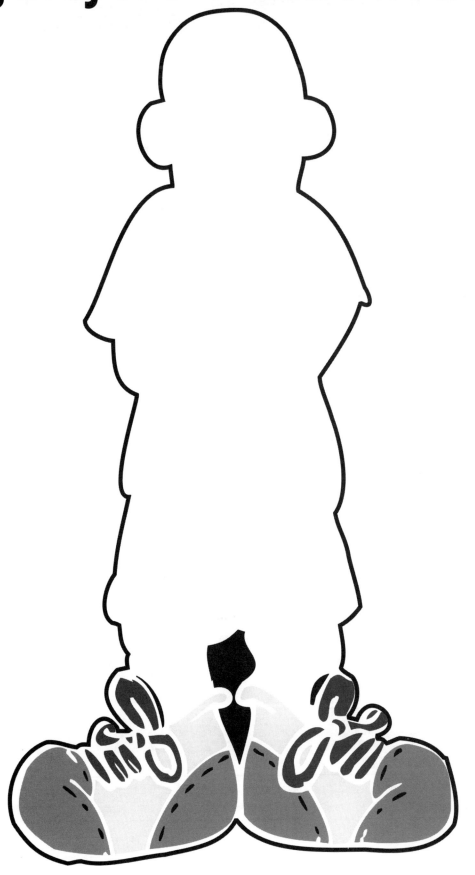

EMOTIONAL AWARENESS 4-10
COLORFUL COUNSELING! © 2006 MAR✶CO PRODUCTS, INC. 1-800-448-2197

I Can Share
MY FEELINGS

Joyful PROUD MAD
surprised
lonely

A LIST OF FEELINGS WORDS

There are many feelings words. *Happy, sad, scared,* and *mad* are just the beginning! Here are just a few:

afraid	enraged	nervous
alarmed	exasperated	overwhelmed
amazed	excited	peaceful
angry	exuberant	perplexed
annoyed	fearful	pleased
anxious	frightened	proud
apprehensive	frustrated	puzzled
ashamed	furious	relaxed
astonished	glad	relieved
bashful	guilty	remorseful
bewildered	happy	sad
blissful	humiliated	scared
bored	hurt	shocked
calm	impatient	shy
cheerful	intimidated	sorrowful
confused	irritated	startled
contented	jealous	stressed
delighted	joyful	surprised
depressed	jubilant	tense
disappointed	livid	terrified
discouraged	lonely	thrilled
distressed	loved	timid
ecstatic	mad	unhappy
elated	melancholy	upset
embarrassed	miserable	worried

Shy

EXCITED GLAD angry

LIFE LESSON LEARNED

I HAVE FEELINGS THAT I CAN SHARE

SECTION 5 - LOSS
Life Lesson Learned: I Can Feel Better If I Express My Feelings

Loss is a general term that can encompass many ideas. It means that something or someone that was once an important part of someone's life has gone. When the term is used, the first thing many people think of is that someone has experienced the death of a loved one, but the feeling of loss could be the result of many situations. The end of a marriage, having to move to a new house, or the end of a dream could each be considered a loss. The pages in this section will allow children to express their emotions over the loss of something or someone important in their lives.

Counselors should not assume that all children feel a certain way when they have experienced loss. A child *might* feel sadness at the death of a close relative, scared by the funeral experience, or relieved because the person had been sick for a long time and the illness disrupted family life. Every person experiences grief and loss in his/her own personal way.

Young children also don't always understand the permanence of death. They may be more upset at seeing the adults in their lives cry than they are at the death of a grandparent or other family member. Children may ask, "When is Grandpa coming back?" after the death of their grandfather. Explaining *death* in concrete terms is helpful when trying to convey this abstract concept to a small child. "Remember when your bike broke and we couldn't fix it? The doctors tried to help Grandpa get better, but they couldn't make his body well again."

The following pages can be chosen according to their relevance to the situation. Making a booklet about the death of a loved one can be comforting to a child. Choose pages that will be appropriate for the child who has experienced some type of loss. Keep the directions for drawing very general so the child will express the feelings that need to be expressed. Telling the child what to draw will take away from the purpose of these pages, which is expression of feelings.

DIRECTIONS

LOSS: PAGE 5-1
SOMETHING HAS HAPPENED (Title Page)
Have the children complete this page by filling in the blanks and coloring the title words (*Something Has Happened)*. This title is purposefully vague so that it can be used in numerous situations.

LOSS: PAGE 5-2
MY PET IS MISSING
Pets play a big role in a child's life. If the dog got loose, the cat got outside, or the hamster got out of its cage, the child might have difficulty concentrating in class. Again, the counselor can't assume what children might be feeling. On the *Lost!* poster, have the children draw what comes to mind.

LOSS: PAGE 5-3
MY PET HAS DIED
The death of a pet can be an enormous loss to a child—sometimes as great or greater than the loss felt over the death of a human relative. Have the children draw what comes to mind.

LOSS: PAGE 5-4
MY FRIEND HAS DIED
The death of another child can be truly frightening. It might be the first time children realize that if someone their age can die, they can die. Have the children draw what comes to mind.

LOSS: PAGE 5-5
SOMEONE IN MY FAMILY HAS DIED
The experience of having a death in the family can be very frightening for children. Not only did the child lose an important person, but death becomes very real and the child begins to imagine Mother, Father, or other close relatives dying. Have the children draw what comes to mind.

LOSS: PAGE 5-6
MY FRIEND IS MOVING AWAY
This topic can present a huge loss for children. On the top half of the page, have the children draw what comes to mind. In the bottom section, have the children draw ways they might keep in touch with friends who have moved.

LOSS: PAGE 5-7
MY FAMILY IS PLANNING TO MOVE
Moving can be very traumatic for children. They are losing their friends, school, comfort zone, and the physical dwelling which represented security or at the least familiarity. Even when the move is made for exciting and happy reasons, there is still a sense of loss. When the move is a result of a breakup of a family or loss of income, it can definitely be painful for children. On the top half of the paper, have the children draw their current home. On the bottom half, have the children draw the new dwelling. (If they haven't seen the new home, have them draw what it might look like.)

LOSS: PAGE 5-8
SOMEONE IN MY FAMILY IS MOVING OUT OF OUR HOUSE
It is threatening, scary, and sad when the family core changes. A parent leaving home or an older brother or sister going away for college can make a huge impact on a child. Have the children draw what comes to mind.

LOSS: PAGE 5-9
MY PARENT IS AWAY ON A TRIP
Teachers can usually tell when a parent is away. Children often are clingy, nervous, or just act "different." Inside the suitcase, have the children draw what comes to mind.

LOSS: PAGE 5-10
HAPPY MEMORIES
It is always comforting to remember happy times shared with a loved one who has left home or died. Let the children draw several memories that can be kept close when they are feeling sad. Tell the children that this piece of paper isn't necessary to remember happy memories. Children can keep these thoughts in mind for comfort when the feelings of sadness or hurt are present.

COLORFUL COUNSELING! © 2006 MAR∗CO PRODUCTS, INC. 1-800-448-2197

LOSS: PAGE 5-11
WHAT I CAN DO TO FEEL BETTER
Have the children draw four ways they can feel better when they are sad, scared, or upset. Ideas might include getting a hug from a loved one, thinking of good memories, talking with someone, going out to play, watching TV, doing something active, or enjoying an activity.

LOSS: PAGE 5-12
WHO WILL LISTEN?
There are similar pages in other sections of this book, but the topic bears repeating and is very appropriate when talking about loss. If a grandparent has died, children might be hesitant to talk with their mom or dad, fearing that mentioning the person who has died will make them feel sad. Assure the children that talking might be helpful to all of them because the family can share the sad feelings everyone is having. Tell the children that tears can be a helpful way to express feelings, so crying may help parents express their feelings about the loss. Assure children that there is always someone who will want to listen. Have the children draw pictures of people who would want to know how they are feeling.

LOSS: PAGE 5-13
LIFE LESSON LEARNED –
I CAN FEEL BETTER IF I EXPRESS MY FEELINGS
As the children color the words, stress the idea that everyone experiences loss at some time, but that expressing feelings through drawing or talking can help them get through the sadness.

SOMETHING HAS HAPPENED

I feel empty and sad,
Like I'll never be the same.
I need someone to help and
Pull me through this pain.

My memories can comfort me,
In time I will be able to think
Of just my love and happy times,
The sadness will gradually shrink.

MY NAME IS

_____

GRADE _____ DATE _____

LOSS 5-1

My Pet Is Missing

LOST!

MY PET HAS DIED

LOSS 5-3
COLORFUL COUNSELING! © 2006 MAR*CO PRODUCTS, INC. 1-800-448-2197

MY FRIEND HAS DIED

SOMEONE IN MY FAMILY HAS DIED

LOSS 5-5
COLORFUL COUNSELING! © 2006 MAR*CO PRODUCTS, INC. 1-800-448-2197

My Friend Is Moving Away

Ways I can keep in touch with my friend:

My Family Is Planning To Move

This is where I live now ...

This is where I will live ...

Someone In My Family Is Moving Out Of Our House

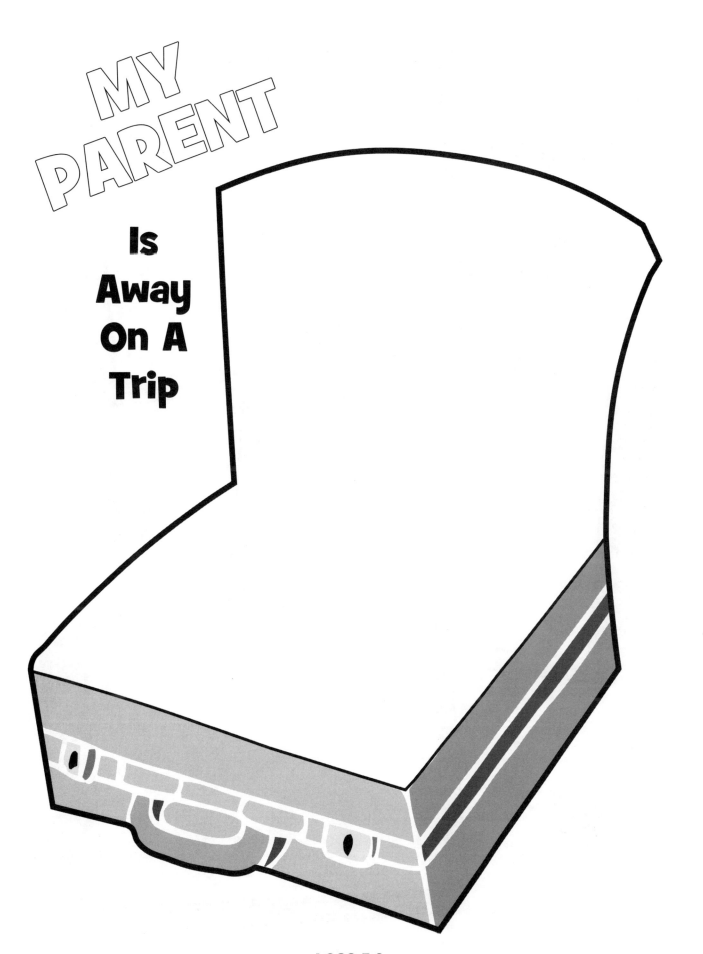

MY PARENT

Is
Away
On A
Trip

LOSS 5-9
COLORFUL COUNSELING! © 2006 MAR*CO PRODUCTS, INC. 1-800-448-2197

HAPPY
Memories

WHAT I CAN DO TO FEEL BETTER

LIFE LESSON LEARNED

I CAN FEEL BETTER IF I EXPRESS MY FEELINGS

SECTION 6 - ANGER
Life Lesson Learned: I Can Calm Down When I Am Angry!

Anger is an emotion that can certainly cause trouble. A person who loses control can destroy property and hurt or even kill another person in the heat of an angry moment. Through examples and discussion, children must be made aware of how destructive uncontrolled anger can be. They must learn that people can manage their tempers if they desire to do so.

Many young children have learned that they can get into trouble for getting mad, but they don't often know what to do with the emotion when they experience it. Their angry feelings sometimes surface as inappropriate behavior or temper tantrums.

After displaying this type of outburst, some children don't take responsibility for their actions. They blame their behavior on a "bad temper" or they were not able to control themselves. But children should be taught that anger does not excuse anyone from violent acts or bad behavior and that people *can* calm themselves before they lose control.

These pages have been designed with the assumption that the child is having difficulty with anger. The counselor should stress that there is an important sequence to learn: *First* an angry person must calm down. Only *then* can problem-solving take place.

ANGER

DIRECTIONS

ANGER: PAGE 6-1
SOMETIMES I GET ANGRY (Title Page)
Have the children fill in the information at the bottom of the page, then color the page. Explain that anger is a human emotion. It is not *wrong* to get angry, but it *is* wrong to express anger in a violent manner. Children should be taught at an early age that they can and must learn to control their tempers.

ANGER: PAGE 6-2
EVERYONE GETS ANGRY ONCE IN A WHILE!
Have the children draw the way they look when they are mad. Looking in a mirror to recognize the facial changes of a "mad face" will help them recognize what the feeling looks like on their faces, as well as on the faces of other people. Staying away from an angry person can be an important life lesson!

ANGER: PAGE 6-3
THIS IS HOW MY BODY FEELS WHEN I AM ANGRY!
Have the children use the outline of the body to identify areas where they feel anger. They can do this by drawing a flame in that part of the body or drawing a knot or using some other illustration to show how they feel. Then have the children complete the sentences at the bottom of the page. When learning how to manage and control anger, one of the first things children must do is become familiar with physical changes which occur as their tempers rise. For example, a child who discovers that his/her muscles tighten and who holds his/her breath when angry, can use these symptoms as a warning to begin using calming techniques.

ANGER: PAGE 6-4
I WANT TO LEARN TO CONTROL MY TEMPER BECAUSE:
Have the children draw four reasons why they might want to learn to control their tempers. If any of the children have trouble thinking of reasons, ask what can happen to a person who loses his/her temper. This would be a great time to teach the word *consequences*.

ANGER: PAGE 6-5
THIS IS WHEN I FEEL MAD
Have the children identify and draw four situations that tend to make them mad. Tell them that if they can recognize the type of situation that angers them, they may be able to catch their anger at an early stage and calm down. Using this information with their body symptoms from page 6-3 will help them realize when it is time to calm down.

ANGER: PAGE 6-6
I COULD GET MAD BECAUSE OF A MISUNDERSTANDING
Ask the children if they have ever gotten mad at someone, then found out it was an accident or a misunderstanding. (For example, someone kicked you and you thought it was done on purpose, so you got mad and kicked the person back. Then you found out that the person tripped and didn't mean to kick you.) After discussing this type of misunderstanding, have the children write their situation on the lines and draw a picture of this type of mistaken anger.

ANGER: PAGE 6-7
WAYS I CAN CALM DOWN
This page lists many ways that people use to calm themselves down. If the children know of other ways to calm down, add them to the list.

ANGER: PAGE 6-8
MY FAVORITE WAYS TO CALM DOWN
Have the children look at the list on page 6-7 to determine the ways that work best for them. Have them choose three ways and draw a picture of themselves using those methods to calm down.

ANGER: PAGE 6-9
ONCE I AM CALM, I CAN WORK THROUGH MY PROBLEM
Once children are taught ways to control their tempers, they can learn to solve the problems that triggered the temper flares. Anger usually arises as the result of a problem or injustice as seen through the eyes of the angry person. It can often be a self-defense mechanism that kicks in when a person feels unfairly treated. Therefore, children should be encouraged to use problem-solving steps to find a solution for the problem that triggered the anger and make each situa-

tion a learning experience. Then, when they face a similar situation again, they will know how to handle the problem without violence or explosions. Have the children draw a picture of themselves calmly talking with another person. Reinforce the idea that this can only happen if all people involved are CALM!

ANGER: PAGE 6-10
PROBLEM-SOLVING MADE EASY!
Repeatedly reinforce the idea that a person must calm down before he/she can solve a problem. Have the children write down a problem they are having and fill in the blanks of the "I Message." Have them color the letters that say *#1 Calm Down*. On the bottom half of the sheet, have the children brainstorm and draw some solutions to the problem. Lastly, have them circle the solution that seems best.

ANGER: PAGE 6-11
LIFE LESSON LEARNED - I CAN CALM DOWN WHEN I AM ANGRY!
The important lesson is that everyone can calm down if he/she desires to do so. As the children color the words, reinforce the idea that situations can be resolved if the person learns to first calm down.

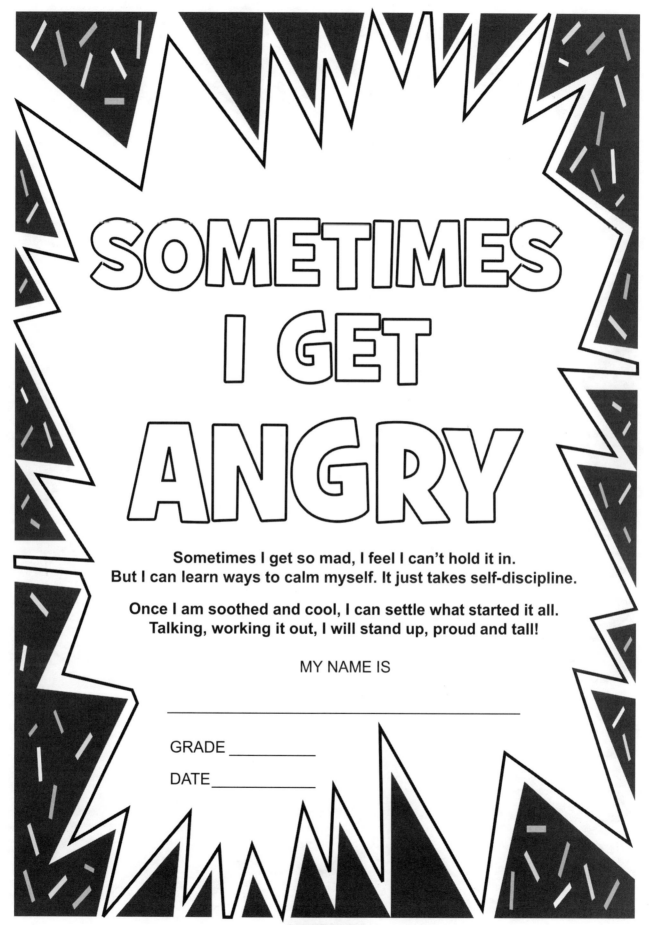

SOMETIMES I GET ANGRY

Sometimes I get so mad, I feel I can't hold it in.
But I can learn ways to calm myself. It just takes self-discipline.

Once I am soothed and cool, I can settle what started it all.
Talking, working it out, I will stand up, proud and tall!

MY NAME IS

_____

GRADE _____

DATE _____

ANGER 6-1

Everyone Gets Angry Once In A While!

This is a picture of me when I get angry!

ANGER 6-2

This Is How My Body Feels When I Am

ANGRY!

My head feels _____ .

My muscles feel _____ .

My heart feels _____ .

My stomach feels _____ .

Other places inside me that feel anger are _____

_____ .

ANGER 6-3

I Want To Learn To Control My Temper Because:

Draw four reasons you should learn to CALM DOWN when you are angry.

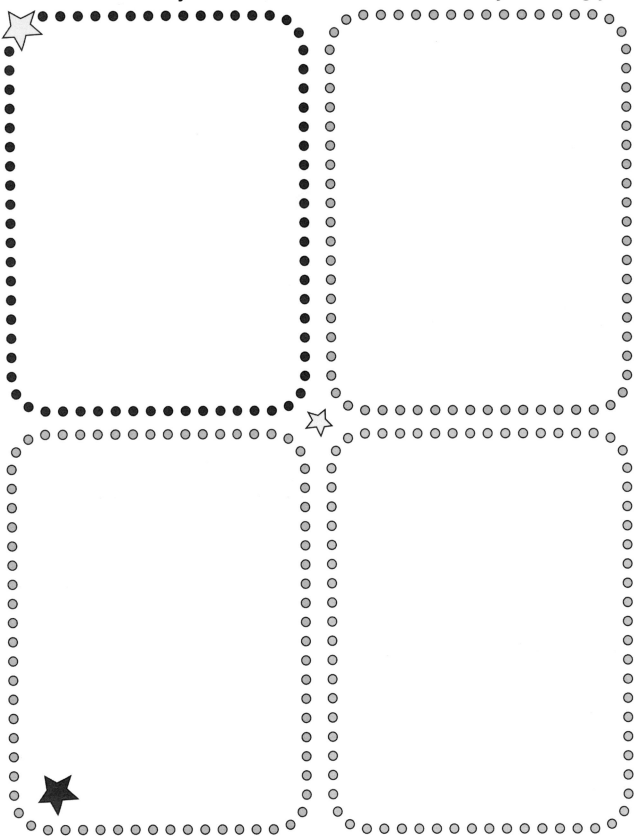

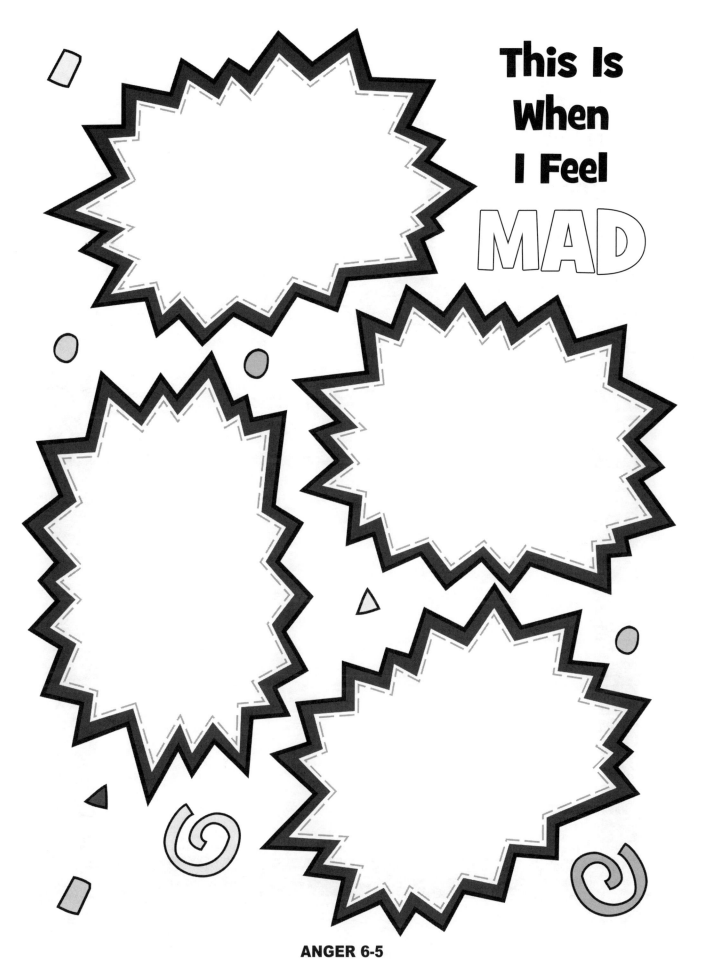

This Is When I Feel **MAD**

I Could Get MAD

Because Of A Misunderstanding

I thought _____

_____

_____ ,

but it didn't happen that way.

THIS IS WHAT REALLY HAPPENED:

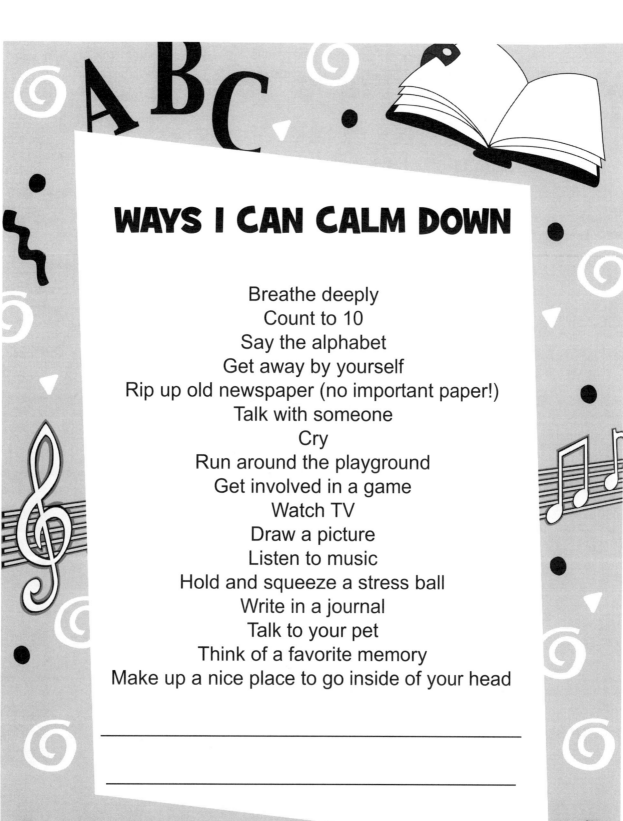

WAYS I CAN CALM DOWN

Breathe deeply
Count to 10
Say the alphabet
Get away by yourself
Rip up old newspaper (no important paper!)
Talk with someone
Cry
Run around the playground
Get involved in a game
Watch TV
Draw a picture
Listen to music
Hold and squeeze a stress ball
Write in a journal
Talk to your pet
Think of a favorite memory
Make up a nice place to go inside of your head

_____

_____

ANGER 6-7

My Favorite Ways To CALM DOWN

Here are three of my favorite ways to calm down!

 **Idea #1**

 **Idea #2**

 **Idea #3**

This is me,

calm and talking with someone about my problem.

Problem-Solving Made Easy!

My problem is _____ .

I feel _____ because _____

and I want to _____ .

#1 CALM DOWN

Some solutions to my problem could be:

 Circle the solution that seems best to you.

LIFE LESSON LEARNED

I CAN CALM DOWN WHEN I AM ANGRY!

SECTION 7 - FEARS AND WORRIES

Life Lesson Learned: I Can Get Help When I Am Scared Or Worried

The world can be a scary place for children who feel that they have little control over their lives. Children have to depend on the adults in their lives to make all the big decisions for them. They don't get to decide where they live, what to do if their family doesn't have enough money for basic necessities, with whom they will live … and the list goes on. Not having any control can make a child feel totally anxious and powerless.

While some children are well provided for and have supportive, loving adults in their lives, some are surrounded by poverty or violence in their homes, neighborhoods, or at school. Even children who live in peaceful, loving homes may see movies, TV programs, or news shows that might worry or scare them. It is easy to see why many children endure stress, nervousness, worries, fears, and anxiety on a daily basis.

Children often don't know how to use words to talk about their problems. Fears, worries, and anxieties locked inside children may manifest into problems of misbehavior, poor health, or depression. Some children develop phobias, experience nightmares, or have health problems—all because of inability to express their fears or worries in appropriate ways. Some children, suffering from anxiety, are not even able to recognize that there is a focus to the problems they are experiencing. Helping children express their feelings should be an important goal of an elementary counselor.

Using these pages, the counselor can help children learn that expressing fears and worries can bring some relief and changing their thoughts about a situation can help change the feelings which were triggered by these thoughts.

DIRECTIONS

FEARS AND WORRIES: PAGE 7-1

SOMETIMES I FEEL SCARED AND WORRIED (Title Page)

Tell the children that all people, no matter how big or strong they may be, feel scared or worried sometimes. Have the children color the page and fill in the information at the bottom of the page.

FEARS AND WORRIES: PAGE 7-2

I FEEL SCARED WHEN ...

Encourage the children to think of things that scare them. Tell them to draw whatever comes to mind. As the children draw, be alert for any changes that may come over their faces or mannerisms.

FEARS AND WORRIES: PAGE 7-3

WORRIES ABOUT MY FAMILY

Ask the children to tell you about their families (see Section 3). Have them draw a worry they might have about a family member. Ask whether the worry is a "child-sized worry" or an "adult worry." Discuss the difference between the kind of worry over which children have some control and the type over which they have no control.

FEARS AND WORRIES: PAGE 7-4

I WORRY ABOUT ...

Discuss the meaning of the word *worry*. Ask the children to draw something they sometimes worry about. This title is purposely vague and children should be encouraged to draw the first thing that comes to mind.

FEARS AND WORRIES: PAGE 7-5

A NIGHTMARE I HAD

Have the children draw a picture of a nightmare they have had. Tell them that nightmares come from thoughts and can be managed by planting positive thoughts and creating a pleasant bedtime routine. Have the children think of a positive message they can say to themselves at bedtime.

FEARS AND WORRIES: PAGE 7-6
I SAW SOMETHING THAT SCARED ME
This worksheet might be appropriate for use with children who have witnessed some type of tragic or scary event. Have them draw a picture of the situation.

FEARS AND WORRIES: PAGE 7-7
SOMETHING BAD HAPPENED
The title of this worksheet is purposely vague. Drawing can be used to help children express feelings about a situation that is bothering them.

FEARS AND WORRIES: PAGE 7-8
MY BODY FEELS WORRIED
Have the children use the outline to show in their bodies where they feel worries. Some people get headaches, some stomachaches, or some might clench their teeth. Tell the children that drawing about or talking about their worries is one way to get their bodies to relax. Teach the children to do relaxation exercises by pretending their bodies have no bones or by taking deep, big breaths.

FEARS AND WORRIES: PAGE 7-9
I WISH I COULD CHANGE SOMETHING ABOUT MY PROBLEM
Have the children make a wish that would resolve their worries or fears. The important point is to ask and answer the question at the bottom of the page: *Do I have the power to make this wish come true?* Children can learn to change situations over which they have power and change the way they *think* about situations over which they have *no* power, but they must recognize the difference.

FEARS AND WORRIES: PAGE 7-10
CHANGES I CAN MAKE
If the children have recognized that there are some changes they could make to improve the situation causing them fear or worry, they should make those changes. For example, a child who is worried that someone will kidnap him/her can walk with a group, ride the bus if possible, take the most populated ways to school, etc. Have the children draw a picture of some changes they could make to resolve their problems.

FEARS AND WORRIES: PAGE 7-11
I CAN CHANGE MY THOUGHTS
Children must learn that there is sometimes nothing they can do to directly elimi-nate the problem, but that they can change their thinking about a situation. A child who is worried about the state of world affairs, for example, cannot change the situation, but can change the way he/she thinks about it. The child can think, "I can't change the world, but I can get involved in helping my neighbors" or "I will get busy at school and do the best I can to make my own life positive." In the bubbles, have the children list or draw some positive thoughts to help them-selves feel better about their worries or fears.

FEARS AND WORRIES: PAGE 7-12
THIS IS WHO CAN HELP ME WITH MY WORRIES
Have the children draw a picture of a person or persons they trust and who can help them with their problems. Help the children realize that talking with a friend can help, but sometimes they must talk with an adult in authority, who can help change the situation. Explain that expressing their feelings to trusted adults will help them feel more power to face the world with a positive attitude.

FEARS AND WORRIES: PAGE 7-13
LIFE LESSON LEARNED -
I CAN GET HELP WHEN I AM SCARED OR WORRIED
As the children color the words, reinforce the idea that children should not keep worries or fears to themselves. Someone is always there to listen and help.

SOMETIMES I FEEL SCARED AND WORRIED

I sometimes feel so scared when I think of bad things that could be.
Especially at night when it's dark, my mind seems to roam and go free.

I know that it helps to talk about my worries, anxiety, and fear.
Confiding in someone I trust will help my head feel clear.

MY NAME IS

_____

GRADE _____   DATE_____

FEARS AND WORRIES 7-1

I Feel Scared When ...

Worries About My
FAMILY

FEARS AND WORRIES 7-4
COLORFUL COUNSELING! © 2006 MAR*CO PRODUCTS, INC. 1-800-448-2197

A Nightmare I Had

I SAW SOMETHING THAT SCARED ME

FEARS AND WORRIES 7-6

Something Bad Happened

My Body Feels Worried

Worries come from my thoughts, but I also feel worries and fear in different places in my body. This is where I feel my worries.

I Wish I Could Change Something About My Problem

Do I have the power
to make this wish come true?

_____
Yes or No?

CHANGES I Can Make

I Can Change MY Thoughts

This Is Who Can Help Me With My Worries

LIFE LESSON LEARNED

I CAN GET HELP WHEN I AM SCARED OR WORRIED

SECTION 8 - BEHAVIOR
Life Lesson Learned: I Am In Control Of My Own Behavior

Because children are frequently referred due to their behavior, the counselor must help children understand that actions have consequences and that they must take responsibility for their behavior. Good behavior should lead to good consequences and poor behavior should lead to poor consequences. A person who frequently exhibits good behaviors is a good citizen and good citizenship is vital to success in life.

The pages in this section will help children understand the concept of *consequences* and why being a good citizen is rewarding. Specific behaviors that should be encouraged (helping, using kind words, voting) are addressed, so are behaviors that should be avoided (stealing, cheating, lying).

After completing the pages in this section, the children will be asked to tell *why* they should be good citizens and behave well. Most importantly, children will learn that they are in control of their own behavior.

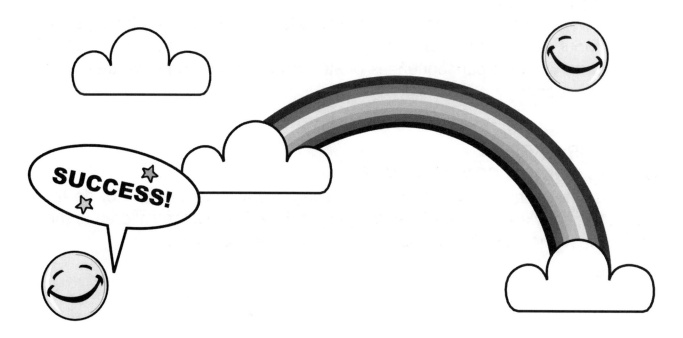

DIRECTIONS

BEHAVIOR: PAGE 8-1

GOOD BEHAVIOR EQUALS GOOD CONSEQUENCES (Title Page)

As the children color the title, ask them to define *consequence*. If they do not know what a consequence is, present the following scenario and see if they can identify the consequence: "Carla stole some candy from the teacher, so Carla had to call her mom and tell her what she had done. Explain that a *consequence* is what happens as a result of a behavior. Ask the children who controlled Carla's behavior. It was Carla who decided to steal the candy, so Carla was the one who had to face the consequences.

BEHAVIOR: PAGE 8-2

A CONSEQUENCE IS WHAT HAPPENS TO ME BECAUSE OF A BEHAVIOR

Sample situations are shown on the left-hand side of the page. On the right-hand side, have the children draw what consequence might result from each action. For example, the child studying for the test might get a good grade, the child helping the elderly man across the street might feel happy, and smoking might get someone sick or could make someone start coughing. Discuss how good behaviors equal good consequences (feeling happy, getting a good grade) and bad behaviors equal bad consequences (coughing, getting into trouble).

BEHAVIOR: PAGE 8-3

STEALING HAS A CONSEQUENCE

Discuss what constitutes *stealing*. (*Stealing* is taking something without permission, without paying for it, or not giving something back that was borrowed.) Ask the children what the consequences of stealing might be and have them draw one consequence.

BEHAVIOR: PAGE 8-4

CHEATING HAS A CONSEQUENCE

Discuss what constitutes *cheating*. (*Cheating* is when people do not do their own work, copy answers, or do not play a game fairly.) Ask the children to think of the consequences of cheating and draw one consequence.

BEHAVIOR: PAGE 8-5
LYING HAS A CONSEQUENCE

Discuss what constitutes *lying*. (*Lying* is not telling the truth or failing to tell the *entire* truth.) Make sure the children know what *truth* means—telling what actually happened. Some children exaggerate facts to get attention. This is also lying. It is a lie to say your family drove to the beach for a vacation, for example, when the family actually stayed at home. Ask the children to think of the consequences of lying and draw one consequence.

BEHAVIOR: PAGE 8-6
KICKING OR HITTING HAS A CONSEQUENCE

Teachers frequently remind children to keep their hands and feet to themselves. Whether the touching is bothersome to another child or is a full-fledged fight, these incidents can be prevented. Ask the children to think of the consequences of fighting or bothering another child and draw one consequence.

BEHAVIOR: PAGE 8-7
FOLLOWING SCHOOL RULES HAS A CONSEQUENCE

By now, the children should realize that negative behaviors will have negative consequences. Now it is time to discuss that following the rules also has consequences, but they will be desirable consequences! Have the children think of a consequence of following school rules and draw one consequence.

BEHAVIOR: PAGE 8-8
GOOD CITIZENS EXHIBIT GOOD BEHAVIORS

In each of the first two flags, have the children draw a good behavior a good citizen might perform. In the flag marked "child's own idea," have the children draw what they could do to show good behavior.

BEHAVIOR: PAGE 8-9
I CAN GIVE THE GIFT OF KINDNESS

One of the best ways to be a good citizen is to be kind to other people. *Kindness* includes what a person says and does. One of the behaviors many children have difficulty with is how to be honest without hurting another person. Remind the children that the old adage, "If you can't say something nice, don't say anything at all" sometimes works. Role-play situations in which the children practice being kind when given a gift they don't like, asked an opinion, and other situations that may arise for a child of this age. In each box, have the children draw a way they can be kind.

Additional Idea: Prepare a gift box with suggestions of nice things children can do or say written on slips of paper. Have the children draw the slips of paper from the gift box. Explain that when people give the gift of kindness, it usually comes back to them.

BEHAVIOR: PAGE 8-10
THIS IS WHY I WANT TO BEHAVE WELL
Ask the children what they believe is the ultimate benefit of good behavior. The answer could be success in life and good self-esteem. In the award ribbon, have the children draw their own reason for behaving well. Have the children discuss how they feel inside when they behave well.

BEHAVIOR: PAGE 8-11
LIFE LESSON LEARNED - I AM IN CONTROL OF MY OWN BEHAVIOR
As the children color in the letters of this concluding statement, the counselor should reinforce the idea that each person is in charge of his/her own behavior!

GOOD BEHAVIOR EQUALS GOOD CONSEQUENCES

I know that I make choices each day at home and school.
I can be rude, mean, or bad, or follow the *Golden Rule.*

What I decide to do affects the people around me.
When I choose what is right, family and friends will surround me.

MY NAME IS

_____

GRADE _____

DATE _____

BEHAVIOR 8-1

A Consequence Is What Happens To Me Because Of A Behavior

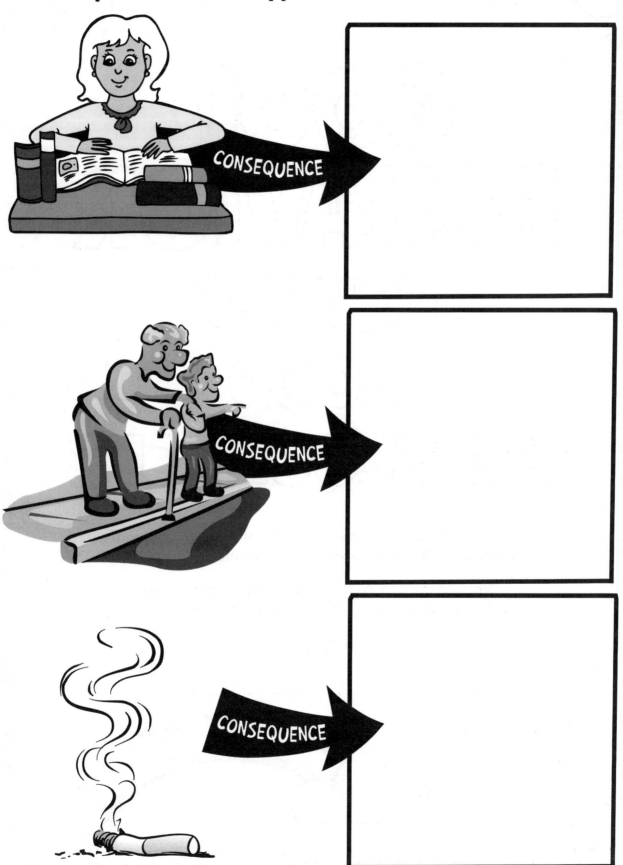

STEALING
HAS A CONSEQUENCE

CHEATING
HAS A CONSEQUENCE

KICKING OR HITTING
HAS A CONSEQUENCE

BEHAVIOR 8-7

Good Citizens Exhibit

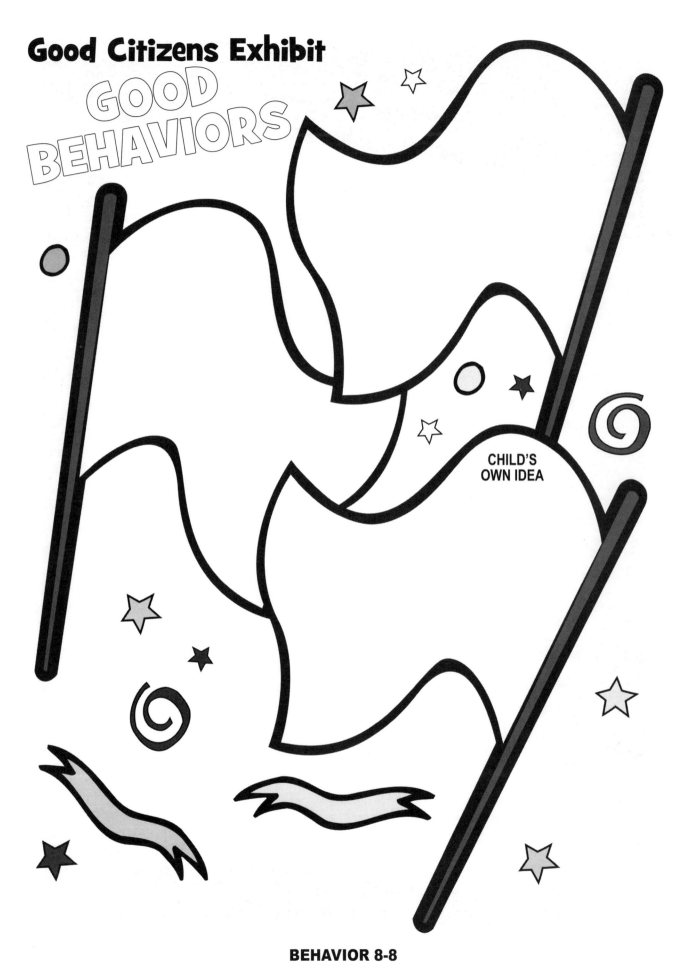

CHILD'S OWN IDEA

I Can Give The Gift Of Kindness

This Is Why I Want To Behave Well

LIFE LESSON LEARNED

SECTION 9 - SCHOOL
Life Lesson Learned: I Can Be A Good Student

School can be a frustrating obligation for some children and an exciting opportunity for others. Counselors know that not all children love going to school, but can try to help unwilling participants feel at ease and realize that getting a good education is an important beginning to a successful life.

The first part of this section (pages 9-1 to 9-7) allows children to express their feelings about school. Pinpointing the area that is bothering a child will enable the counselor to help the child remedy the situation. While the children are drawing, the counselor should carefully observe their facial expressions and mannerisms to help learn how they feel about a particular topic. Listening to what the children say while drawing will provide further clues.

The second part of this section (pages 9-8 to 9-14) covers character-education topics such as attitude, effort, responsibility, perseverance, cooperation, respect, and the importance of setting goals. An appropriate lesson for unenthusiastic children would be that the effort they put into their childhood "job" will come back to them and that doing their best is important.

The pages in Section 9 were designed with the assumption that the child is having problems in school. However, some of the pages would be appropriate for all children. If the counselor plans to use the character-education worksheets with a larger group, the pages could be used as a follow-up to a guidance lesson on the topics.

DIRECTIONS

SCHOOL: PAGE 9-1
SCHOOL IS MY JOB! (Title Page)
Ask the children to color the words of the title. As they are coloring, the counselor can discuss the fact that all people have jobs—parents may have jobs outside of the home or their jobs may be centered within the home. Remind the children that *their* main job is going to school and being students.

SCHOOL: PAGE 9-2
HERE I AM AT SCHOOL
Have the children write the name of their school in the rectangle at the top of the building and draw themselves at school. The counselor may learn something about the children by observing where (in the school) they draw themselves and what kind of expressions they draw on their faces.

SCHOOL: PAGE 9-3
THIS IS MY TEACHER
Unfortunately, not every student and teacher get along. It would be helpful if the children feel they can be honest about their feelings toward their teacher. Have the children draw a picture of their teacher in the space above the teacher's desk. If the children have more than one teacher, ask them to draw one of their teachers. Watch, as the children draw their pictures, for any clues as to how they feel. If any child complains or expresses negative feelings in any way, listen and validate his/her feelings. Explain that learning to get along with others is a part of life. Ask the children to orally list positive traits their teacher may possess as well as negative ones and tell of some ways they could get along better with their teacher.

SCHOOL: PAGE 9-4
RECESS TIME
Have the children draw a picture of what they typically do at recess. There are many things a counselor can learn from such a picture. Has the child drawn him/herself in the middle of a group of friends or off on the side? Is someone bullying the child? Does the child have friends? Recess can be the root of a problem for many children and the counselor should make careful observations during this assignment.

SCHOOL
COLORFUL COUNSELING! © 2006 MAR∗CO PRODUCTS, INC. 1-800-448-2197

SCHOOL: PAGE 9-5
MY FAVORITE SUBJECT
Have the children draw a picture of what they most enjoy doing at school. Which subject does each child see as his/her strength? (The concept of *strengths* and *weaknesses* are covered in Section 1 – Self. If this topic has not yet been covered, let the children know that everyone has strengths on which he/she can proudly build, as well as weaknesses.)

SCHOOL: PAGE 9-6
A SUBJECT THAT IS DIFFICULT FOR ME
Have the children draw themselves attempting a school task they find difficult. Remind them that no one is perfect and that every person has difficulties. While the children are drawing, try to reinforce the point that no matter how much anyone may struggle with a subject area, with perseverance and a good attitude he/she can improve.

SCHOOL: PAGE 9-7
TESTS ARE A PART OF SCHOOL
Some children suffer from a fear of tests. Letting children express their feelings about tests might help them overcome this fear. Have the children draw a picture of themselves taking a test. While the children have the opportunity to express how they feel about tests, the counselor can use this opportunity to remind them that having a good attitude is an important test-taking skill. Encourage the children to think positive thoughts and prepare for tests by studying and getting a good night's sleep; taking deep, calming breaths; and working carefully during the time provided for the test.

SCHOOL: PAGE 9-8
RESPONSIBILITY PAYS OFF
Discuss the word *responsibility* and make sure the children understand that being *responsible* means doing what is expected of them without being constantly reminded. Ask the children to draw a picture of themselves being responsible. While they are drawing, the counselor can make the point that responsible students are often successful students. How does being responsible pay off? Responsible students get better grades; are recognized by teachers, parents, and fellow students; are given more privileges; and feel a sense of pride. Have the children write their answers at the bottom of the activity sheet.

PERSEVERANCE – THE KEY TO SUCCESS!

Some children are so overwhelmed by failure that they stop trying. Remind the children that if they keep trying to do something, they will eventually improve. On the top half of the page, have the children draw themselves attempting something they currently cannot do. In the lower half, have them draw themselves improving at the same task. What trait comes between *trying* and *succeeding*? *Perseverance!* Discuss the fact that perseverance does not guarantee success, but should bring improvement.

POSITIVE ATTITUDE COUNTS

The winners of any endeavor are often the people who believe they can succeed and try to do their best. Remind the children that people often talk to themselves. What messages are they giving themselves? If they say, "I will never do this," that is probably what will happen. If the message is, "I am going to do this!" that will be more likely to happen. Have the children draw pictures of themselves in the star, then write a positive message in the thought bubble.

I CAN SET GOALS TO WIN!

Setting a goal means deciding to do something positive. The person must make a plan to accomplish a goal. Ask the children to name a goal they would like to reach. Remind them that the goal must be *realistic* (something the child can achieve) and should be *measurable* (so the child can tell if he/she has succeeded). Saying "I am going to do better," is not a measurable goal, because it is not clear what better means. It would be a measurable goal to say, "I am going to turn in all of my homework." Inside the trophy, have the children draw themselves achieving their goal.

GOOD WORK HABITS ARE IMPORTANT

Discuss the definition of a *habit*. (A way of doing a task that becomes automatic, such as brushing teeth each night before going to bed. We don't think about it— we just do it.) Tell the children that developing good work habits will help them now and in the future. Have the children draw three good work habits that will help them succeed in school. (Examples might be: writing all assignments in an assignment book, listening in class, doing all assignments, checking work before handing it in, using a book bag, keeping materials organized.)

SCHOOL: PAGE 9-13
WAYS I CAN SHOW RESPECT FOR OTHERS
Showing respect for others is treating people the way you want to be treated. Using good manners is one way of showing respect. Have the children draw four ways they can show respect for others. (Examples of showing respect might be: saying, "Thank you," "I'm sorry," and "Excuse me"; using good sportsmanship; taking turns; sharing; helping others when they need it; determining a fair way to go first; playing fair; etc.)

SCHOOL: PAGE 9-14
COOPERATION MAKES THE SCHOOL DAY HAPPY
A classroom of children who know how to share, take turns, and settle disagreements peacefully is a happy place to be. Have the children draw a picture of a classroom group showing good cooperation skills. Make sure the children draw themselves in this happy picture. (Examples of cooperation might be: sharing, taking turns, smiling at others, voting to determine who goes first, voting to determine group procedures, etc.)

SCHOOL: PAGE 9-15
LIFE LESSON LEARNED: I CAN BE A GOOD STUDENT
As the children color the words, remind them that they can choose whether they are going to be good students.

SCHOOL IS MY JOB!

School is the place where I spend lots of time.
The things I learn there can last a lifetime.
But I'll only find success if I try very hard.
Attitude and effort show on my report card.

Responsibility, listening, and setting high goals
Are the jobs of a student, but just part of the whole.
Good work habits and study skills add to the rest
If I want to succeed, I must try to do my best!

MY NAME IS

_____

GRADE_____

DATE_____

COLORFUL COUNSELING! © 2006 MAR∗CO PRODUCTS, INC. 1-800-448-2197

Here I Am At School

SCHOOL 9-3
COLORFUL COUNSELING! © 2006 MAR*CO PRODUCTS, INC. 1-800-448-2197

RECESS TIME

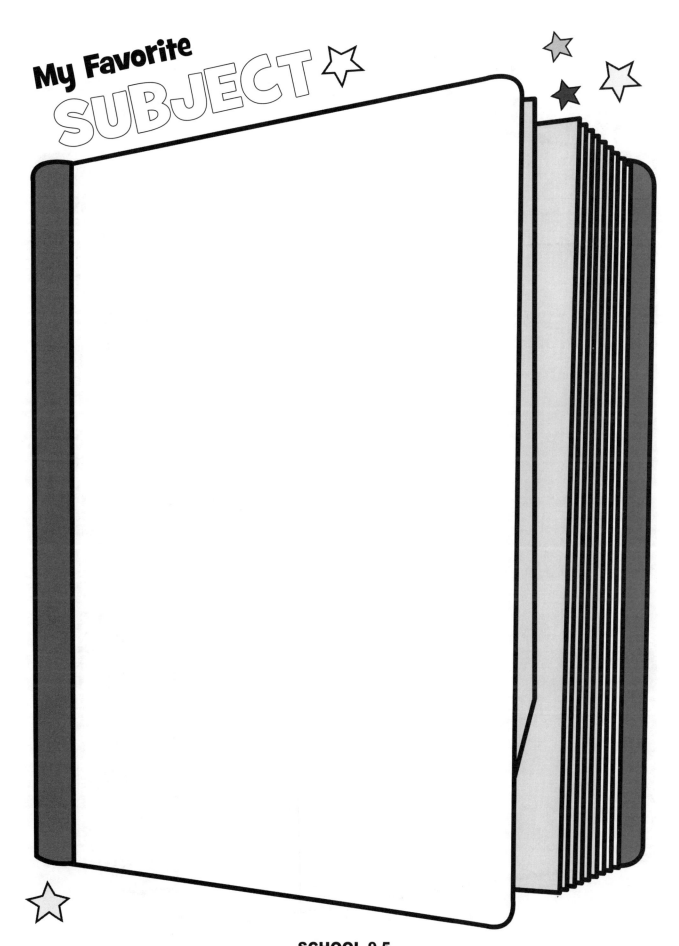

My Favorite SUBJECT

A Subject That Is DIFFICULT For Me

Tests Are A Part Of School

TEST TODAY

RESPONSIBILITY Pays Off

How does responsibility pay off?

_____

_____

PERSEVERANCE
THE KEY TO SUCCESS!

I CAN SET
GOALS TO WIN!

SCHOOL 9-11
COLORFUL COUNSELING! © 2006 MAR✲CO PRODUCTS, INC. 1-800-448-2197

GOOD WORK HABITS

Are Important

Ways I Can Show
RESPECT FOR OTHERS

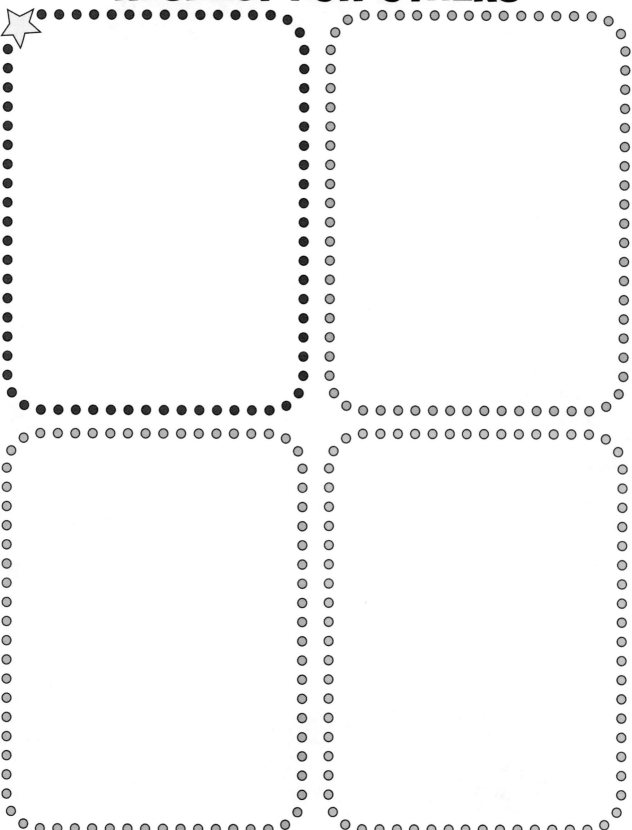

Cooperation Makes The School Day Happy

LIFE LESSON LEARNED

I CAN BE A GOOD STUDENT

SECTION 10 - SAFETY FIRST
Life Lesson Learned: I Know How to Stay Safe

Children should be taught that they can help themselves stay safe by learning to make good choices. While parents try to protect their children from harm, an adult cannot be with a school-age child 24 hours a day. Children must be aware that they do have some power to keep themselves safe by making wise decisions and thinking about safety.

Children are often impulsive and don't always take the time to think before they act, so the first thing they must be taught is to slow down and consider the consequences of their actions. Whether staying safe on the playground or staying away from drugs and alcohol, children should think about and practice good habits.

The pages in this section can be used to help children become aware that the choices they make are important and can have an impact on their safety. Drawing and discussing the messages on these pages can encourage children to think of "Safety First!"

SAFETY FIRST

DIRECTIONS

SAFETY FIRST: PAGE 10-1

I CHOOSE SAFETY FIRST (Title Page)

While the children color the words on this page, discuss what *staying safe* means to them. Emphasize that staying safe should be a priority in life. If children are to have the opportunity to grow up and be successful, they need to stay safe and healthy.

SAFETY FIRST: PAGE 10-2

IN ORDER TO STAY SAFE, I NEED TO MAKE GOOD CHOICES

Children are sometimes faced with potentially dangerous situations. Tragedies happen that might have been prevented if the child thought before acting. This page is designed to help children think about what could happen to them because of the choices they make. There are drawings of dangerous situations on the left-hand side of this page. In the rectangle on the right, have the children draw a safe choice they could make when confronted with this situation. Explain that staying safe starts with the decisions that are made.

SAFETY FIRST: PAGE 10-3

I KNOW HOW TO STAY SAFE ON THE PLAYGROUND

Many accidents happen on the playground. Children must watch where they are going and be aware of what is going on around them. They also need to know to play on equipment appropriate for their age. Little decisions like waiting for someone to get out of the way of the slide before going down can be a big help when trying to avoid injuries. Brainstorm with the children ways to prevent injuries on the playground. Then have the children draw one of these on the activity sheet. (Answers may include: following playground rules, being aware of the activities and games around you, wearing proper shoes, not throwing rocks or snowballs, waiting your turn on equipment, etc.)

SAFETY FIRST: PAGE 10-4

I KNOW HOW TO STAY SAFE ON THE WAY TO AND FROM SCHOOL

Children get to and from school in various ways. From riding in a carpool to walking to the bus, each way can potentially harm a child. Ask the children how they usually get to and from school, then have them draw a way to stay safe

COLORFUL COUNSELING! © 2006 MAR✶CO PRODUCTS, INC. 1-800-448-2197

while doing so. (Pictures may include: wearing seat belts in the car, staying seated on the bus, looking both ways when walking, walking where the bus driver can see them, walking home with a group of children, going directly home after school, etc.)

SAFETY FIRST: PAGE 10-5
I KNOW HOW TO STAY SAFE AT HOME
Some children are *latchkey kids*. These children spend time before and after school by themselves or with other siblings. Because an adult is not always around during these hours, it is especially important that these children know how to keep themselves out of danger. Explore ways children can keep themselves safe and have them draw some ways on the activity sheet. (Examples include: keeping the doors locked; knowing the location of the fire extinguisher; telling phone callers that their parents are busy; staying away from matches, electricity, and medicines; etc.)

SAFETY FIRST: PAGE 10-6
I KNOW HOW TO STAY SAFE IN THE CAR
Children will probably think first about wearing seatbelts. This idea is very valid, of course, but encourage the children to think of additional ways they can stay safe and have them draw a few on the activity sheet. (Examples include: making sure the doors are locked, not distracting the driver, keeping arms and legs in the car, not playing in a parked car, etc.)

SAFETY FIRST: PAGE 10-7
I KNOW I SHOULD TAKE MEDICINE ONLY FROM A TRUSTED ADULT
Children should learn that medicines can help only when taken correctly. Teach children that taking the wrong medicines or taking the wrong dose of the right medicine can make them sick or even kill them. Teach children not to help themselves to medicines, but to take them only when necessary and only from a trusted adult. Have the children draw themselves taking medicine from such an adult.

SAFETY FIRST: PAGE 10-8
I KNOW HOW TO STAY AWAY FROM DRUGS AND ALCOHOL
Experimenting with drugs and alcohol can be disastrous. Children should plan what they would do if someone offered drugs or alcohol to them. Have the children draw what they can do or write what they can say in this situation.

SAFETY FIRST: PAGE 10-9
I KNOW HOW TO MAKE A SAFE CHOICE
IF A STRANGER APPROACHES ME
Children should learn about *stranger danger* early in their lives. Have the children draw what they will do if a stranger approaches them. The counselor should reinforce the fact that children should always let a trusted adult know about any incident that takes place.

SAFETY FIRST: PAGE 10-10
I KNOW WHAT TO DO IF SOMEONE WANTS
TO TOUCH ME IN A WAY THAT MAKES ME UNCOMFORTABLE
Discuss that children have the right to let someone know when they are uncomfortable. If they do not want to be touched, no matter who is touching them on any part of their body, they should tell the person to stop and begin yelling if he/she won't stop. Have the children draw what they will do or write what they will say if they do not like being touched. The counselor should make sure that the children know they should tell a trusted adult about any uncomfortable situations.

SAFETY FIRST: PAGE 10-11
LIFE LESSON LEARNED – I KNOW HOW TO STAY SAFE
As the children color in this message, the counselor should review the ways children have learned to keep themselves safe. Remind the children that they have the power to make choices that will help them stay safe.

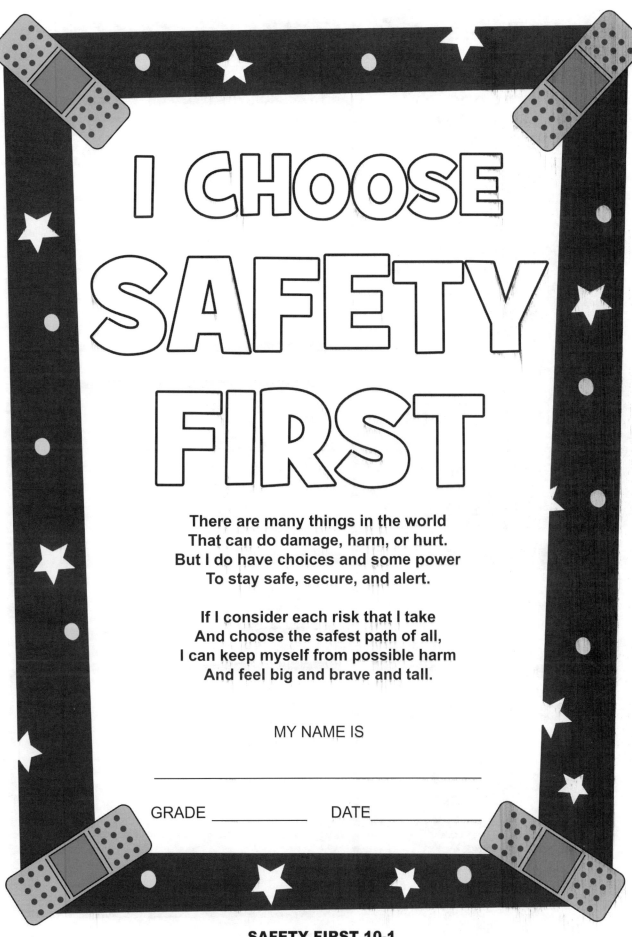

I CHOOSE
SAFETY
FIRST

There are many things in the world
That can do damage, harm, or hurt.
But I do have choices and some power
To stay safe, secure, and alert.

If I consider each risk that I take
And choose the safest path of all,
I can keep myself from possible harm
And feel big and brave and tall.

MY NAME IS

_____

GRADE _____   DATE_____

SAFETY FIRST 10-1

In Order To Stay Safe, I Need To Make Good Choices.

PETTING A DOG YOU
DO NOT KNOW
CAN BE DANGEROUS!

PLAYING WITH MATCHES
CAN BE DANGEROUS!

SWIMMING WITHOUT
AN ADULT
CAN BE DANGEROUS!

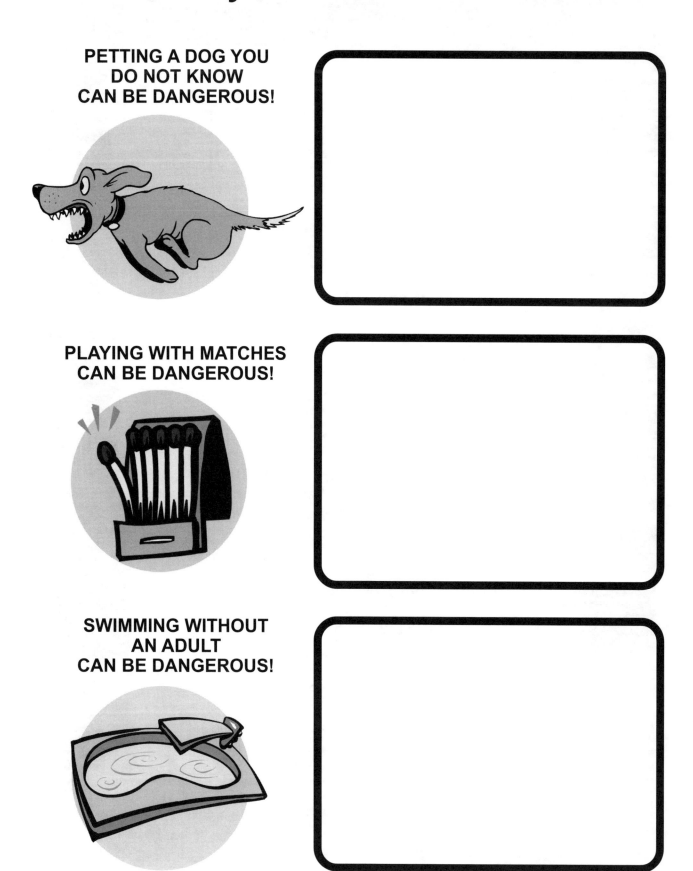

SAFETY FIRST 10-2

I Know How To STAY SAFE On The Playground

I Know How To Stay Safe
On The Way To And From School

I Know How To Stay Safe At Home

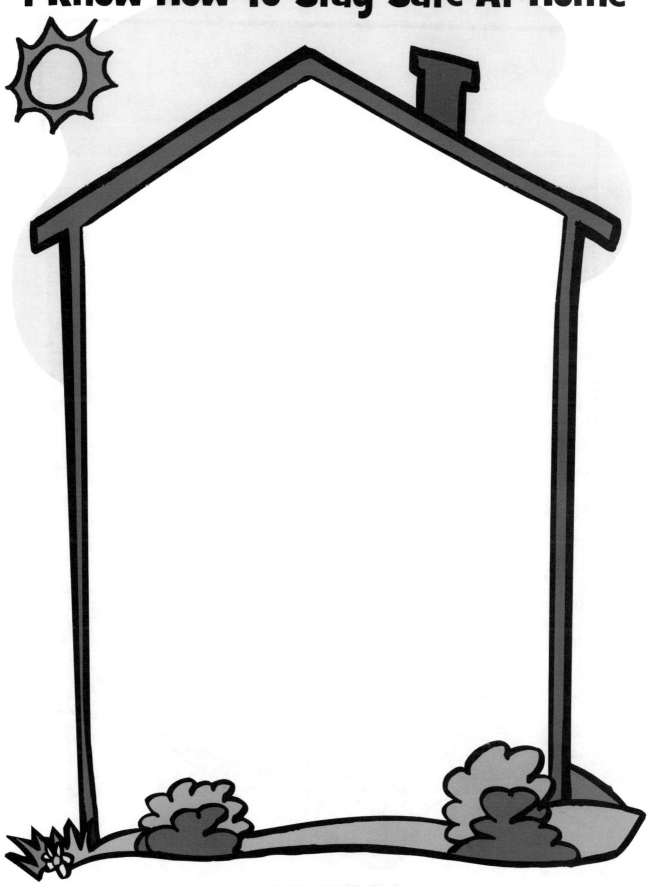

I Know How To Stay Safe In The Car

I Know I Should Take Medicine ONLY From A

TRUSTED ADULT

I Know How To Stay Away From Drugs And Alcohol

I Know How To Make A Safe Choice If

A STRANGER APPROACHES ME

I Know What To Do If Someone Wants To Touch Me In A Way That Makes Me Uncomfortable

I KNOW HOW TO STAY SAFE

ABOUT THE AUTHORS

Rosanne Sheritz Sartori is a retired teacher/counselor and the author of numerous books.

PUBLISHED BY MAR*CO PRODUCTS, INC.

Lively Lessons for Classroom Sessions
More Lively Lessons for Classroom Sessions
Stand Up Against Bullies for Grades K-2
Stand Up Against Bullies for Grades 3-5

Rosanne lives with her husband, Glenn, in St. Louis, Missouri and loves to present her ideas at educational conferences and workshops.

.

Rachel Hood Herrman has her B.A. in psychology from DePauw University and her M.S. in counseling from Indiana University. She worked as an elementary counselor in St. Charles, Missouri before staying home to raise her two children. Rachel lives in Kirkwood, Missouri with her husband, Kyle, and is a happy wife and mother.